FOR BREW FREAKS, BEAN GEEKS, AND THE SIMPLY CURIOUS ...

SOUTH WEST
AND SOUTH WALES
INDEPENDENT
COFFEE
GUIDE

the INSIDER'S GUIDE TO SPECIALITY
COFFEE VENUES AND ROASTERS

★ ★ ★ ★ ★ ★ ★ ★ ★ ★ ★

Nº 4

Salt Media, 5 Cross Street, Devon, EX31 1BA.
www.saltmedia.co.uk
Tel: 01271 859299
Email: ideas@saltmedia.co.uk

Salt Media *Independent Coffee Guide* team:
Nick Cooper, Catherine Courtenay, Lucy Deasy,
Kathryn Lewis, Abi Manning, Tamsin Powell, Jo Rees,
Rosanna Rothery, Christopher Sheppard, Dale Stiling,
Katie Taylor, Mark Tibbles and Harry Wild.
Design and illustration: Salt Media

**A big thank you to the *Independent Coffee Guide*
committee** (meet them on page 184) for their expertise
and enthusiasm, **our headline sponsors** Cimbali,
KeepCup, Schluter and Yeo Valley, **and sponsors**
Almond Breeze, Cakesmiths, Extract Coffee Roasters
and Roastworks Coffee Co.

Coffee shops, cafes and roasters are invited to be
included in the guide based on meeting criteria set by
the committee, which includes a high quality coffee
experience for visitors, use of speciality beans and
being independently run.

For information on the Ireland, The North and North
Wales, and Scottish *Independent Coffee Guides*, visit:

www.indycoffee.guide
🐦 @indycoffeeguide
📷 @indycoffeeguide

MILK TEETH
#25

COFFEE
Roasters

CONTENTS

EXE
COFFEE
ROASTERS
#89

I t's been another great year for speciality coffee as an increasing number of people turn to the good stuff, so I'm chuffed to introduce you to the fourth edition of the *South West & South Wales Independent Coffee Guide.*

We've revisited the mavericks who were fashioning flatties before the chains got a whiff, as well as meeting new kids on the block who are experimenting with filter kit fresh from the lab. It's been a fun (and extremely caffeinated) ride.

This edition has also seen us discovering some of the community initiatives and social enterprises that coffee is supporting – read the Thirst Aid feature on page 14 – and getting the low-down on the rise of the career barista on page 22.

When it comes to finding cafes and roasteries to visit, you'll notice that this year we've moved the roasters next to the cafes in their geographical section, which should make it easier for you to hunt down local beans while coffee shop hopping across the South West and South Wales.

Let us know how you get on as you navigate your way through this caffeine-rich region. We're always keen to see your **#piccoloporn** pics and hear about your new favourites on our Instagram and Twitter feeds.

Kathryn Lewis

Editor

Indy Coffee Guides

🐦 @indycoffeeguide
📷 @indycoffeeguide

Calling all
COFFEE
LOVERS

...show your milk the ♥ you show your beans!

Find out more at yeovalley.co.uk

Yeo Valley organic Whole Milk

Yeo Valley FAMILY FARM

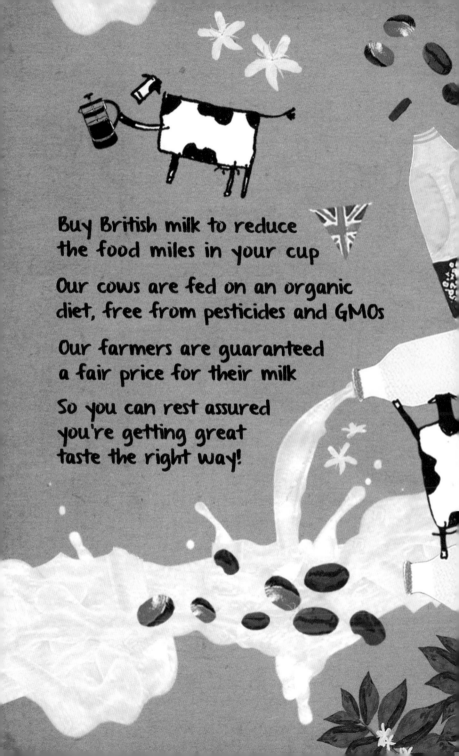

Buy British milk to reduce
the food miles in your cup

Our cows are fed on an organic
diet, free from pesticides and GMOs

Our farmers are guaranteed
a fair price for their milk

So you can rest assured
you're getting great
taste the right way!

THIRST AID

Ensuring coffee farmers receive a fair wage, supporting charities at origin and raising money for local communities – throughout the speciality scene, organisations are going the extra mile to help others.

We met some of the businesses in the South West and South Wales walking the walk

AT ORIGIN
EXTRACT COFFEE ROASTERS

You may have contemplated the barista's handiwork when drinking quality coffee or even the skill of the local roaster who cooked up the beans, but how often have you considered the farmer who cultivated the coffee plant?

It's something that the guys at Extract Coffee Roasters in Bristol think about daily, and which led them to partner up with Sol & Café, a workers' cooperative in Peru.

'Hopping between farms each year to drive down prices is not sustainable,' explains Extract co-founder **DAVID FAULKNER** (pictured). 'We believe in building long-term partnerships which support ongoing and stable growth for our coffee farmers.'

Teaming up with Sol & Café ensures that the farmers supplying Extract are paid a fair price (above the Fairtrade premium). It also provides them with the opportunity to increase the quality of their crops further, for which Extract pays additional incentives and rewards.

The cooperative supplies processing equipment, education and infrastructure which helps the farmers grow coffee of this exceptional quality.

'Working in the cooperative has transformed the community,' adds David. 'Neighbouring farms are building strong relationships with each other, sharing knowledge and skills and forging a vital support network.'

After numerous visits, Extract is working with a group of 50 farmers who, in addition to being part of the cooperative, benefit from a seed fund which the Bristol roastery is building to support community projects.

MANUMIT COFFEE ROASTERS

AT THE ROASTERY

When pastor **DAI HANKEY** was tasked with finding a new platform from which to raise awareness of human trafficking, his interest in speciality coffee inspired a lightbulb moment.

So, with the help of some of the region's best roasters, Dai set up Manumit in South Wales to not only roast exceptional coffee but also to employ and train survivors of modern-day slavery.

Every penny of profit from the Cardiff-roasted coffee goes towards eradicating human trafficking and funding Manumit's barista training programme. The latter, run with the Speciality Coffee Association (SCA), is designed to equip survivors with a skill set to utilise as they begin to rebuild their lives.

'Sadly people often fall back into the industry and there's a high rate of re-trafficking,' explains Dai. 'Coffee is an international phenomenon, and our hope is that the barista skills picked up at Manumit can help survivors to craft a new career – whether that's in the UK or in their native country.'

Dai's currently cooking up a seasonal house blend with the help of Martin and Eva, two survivors who have been developing skills at the roastery since the project launched in June 2017.

'I'm learning just as much as the guys we're supporting,' says Dai. 'And the welcome from the coffee community has been exceptional – we wouldn't be where we are now without their help and kindness.'

AT THE CAFE

For **MATT CROME**, founder of Square Peg, there were two ambitions driving the launch of his Swansea coffee house:

'I'd noticed that there was a gap in society. There was nowhere where people could get together and engage with each other and feel part of a community. At the same time I was fed up with the awful coffee in Swansea and thought I may be able to do something about both,' he explains.

Two years later the social enterprise is thriving, bringing people together for cracking coffee under one roof on Gower Road. All of the profits from the cafe are poured back into the community and fund local homeless charities and projects such as food banks.

It's not just about money though. Square Peg also hosts social events and PegTalks which Matt launched to encourage locals to connect and share stories while discussing important issues ranging from biodiversity to refugees.

The team still find time to excel at speciality though: *'My intention has always been that Square Peg will, first and foremost, be a great coffee shop,'* says Matt. *'It's a competitive market and we still want to push boundaries in terms of coffee, food and service. We just happen to share our profits with those who need it more.'*

Continuing to spread the good vibes, in 2017 a second Peg cafe opened down the road in Mumbles, which is also plunging its extra energy into good causes.

GOOD VIBES BY THE BAG

Scoring speciality beans to brew at home while helping out good causes is a win-win situation, and there are stacks of roasteries across the region which donate money directly from each bag of coffee sold.

At **SABIN'S SMALL BATCH ROASTERS** in Cornwall, one pound from every bag sold of SOS Africa goes to its namesake charity, which raises money to educate children from challenged backgrounds in South Africa.

Meanwhile in Cardiff, the Project Waterfall badge is proudly displayed on every bag of **LUFKIN** roasted beans. Owners Dan and Frances aim to raise awareness of the charity (which brings clean water to coffee-growing communities) and encourage customers to talk about the issues, while giving a donation every month – regardless of the level of sales.

You'll spot **EXTRACT'S** Strong Man espresso on guest spots across the country each November, and not just because the espresso creates an awesome flat white. Aiming to start conversations in coffee shops about men's mental health, the Bristol roaster donates a quid to Movember UK for every kilo sold.

250° COFFEE BEANS   7/8

RIGHT NOW, IN THIS GALAXY
CONSUMPTION OF SINGLE USE ITEMS
THREATENS TO DESTROY
OUR HOME PLANET.
BRING ORDER AND STABILITY
TO THE GALAXY-
TURN AWAY FROM
DISPOSABLE PRODUCTS.

THE FORCE IS STRONG WITH YOU

THE RISE
OF THE
CAREER
BARISTA

Fifteen years ago, if you said you were a barista you'd be pegged as a wig-wearing lawyer. The term 'barista' may no longer be confused with 'barrister' and being an espresso slinger has a certain hipster panache, but what's it like being a professional shot pourer? We got the low-down on the rise of the career barista from some of the region's top tampers ...

TREVOR HYAM is the highly regarded head barista and manager of The Plan in Cardiff. He's been pulling shots since he graduated with a fine art degree in 2004.

'My first foray into coffee was a part-time job in a cafe. I was intrigued and began researching and reading about what was going on in the third wave scene. I moved to The Plan in 2007 and have been there ever since.

'Being a barista is punishingly hard work. It's tiring being on your feet all day and there are lots of less glamorous elements such as clearing tables. As it can be gruelling, you need a passion for coffee to sustain you. It's not just about standing around looking cool; baristas need diligence, a serious work ethic and to be up for continuous learning.

'AS IT CAN BE GRUELLING, YOU NEED A PASSION FOR COFFEE TO SUSTAIN YOU'

'It's still difficult to make a successful long-term career as a barista as opposed to as a coffee consultant or a roaster – especially outside London. It's still not recognised as a serious job outside the industry. Of course, in the coffee world we know how much goes into the craft and the process.

'Part of the issue is there are a limited number of coffee shops which are willing to invest in paying experienced professionals in order to offer their customers really good coffee.

'So it's often a way into other jobs in the coffee world. I love making coffee and serving customers but many others go into competitions and then head off into roasting, coffee hunting or training and consultancy, because it's hard to make a living pulling shots.'

JESSE DODKINS is a 2017 UKBC competitor and Origin's head of education for the South West.

'Compared to 15 years ago, I can think of people who have made a career of being a barista but I still don't think it's recognised as a "serious job". And those who want to take that path don't feel it will offer them security.

'There's also a difference between being a career barista and a coffee professional: career baristas start as a barista and finish as a barista, while the coffee industry also offers a massive chain of different roles, from sourcing to roasting. Often, being a barista is the entry point and people then discover opportunities for themselves elsewhere in the chain.

'The competition element is very central to the career barista as it teaches you to communicate about coffee and affects how you think about it. At Origin, a big part of my role is to focus on competitions and engage with the overall coffee community, as well as train people to be the best barista they can be.

'There is a shortage of very good baristas and our customers struggle to find experienced staff. However, a lot of quality coffee shops don't offer a wage that matches the time that a pro barista spends developing their skill.

'Places that have a great and consistent coffee offering pay their baristas more than those which struggle to find staff or which are less consistent. Baristas shouldn't be paid less just because they have a passion for the job – in fact, that passion should make them more valuable.

'THERE IS A SHORTAGE OF GOOD BARISTAS'

'I was training a really good barista recently who told me that he regularly gets asked, "When are you going to get a real job?". No one asks plumbers when they are going to get a real job. That's why I value the SCA diploma; it shows that it's a skilled job that you train to do.'

'NO ONE ASKS PLUMBERS WHEN THEY ARE GOING TO GET A REAL JOB'

ADRIAN CAMPBELL-HOWARD is the entrepreneur behind the four-strong group of Society Cafes in Bath, Bristol and Oxford. He currently employs around 30 baristas.

'One of the great advantages of learning to be a barista is that it gives you skills that can take you around the world and fund some exciting travels – whether you choose to become a career barista or not,' says Adrian.

'Baristas who join us at Society tend to be full time, even if it's for the shorter term. That's because in speciality cafes serving single estate beans that change all the time, it's difficult to maintain consistency of knowledge unless the baristas are in every day.

'Coming from a hotel and hospitality background, service is very important to us which is why we invest heavily in training. It's key because in speciality, people not only take the product seriously, but also the way it's served.

'We work closely with our main roaster, and when a would-be barista has gone through all of our in-house training we send them off to do the beginner SCA course.

'However, we're aware that many of our baristas also have other interests such as music and graphic design which they may follow eventually, so we try and support those passions too. For example, one of our baristas was studying graphic design while working for us full time in his holidays so we commissioned him to design our cups. He's now embarked on his design career and we're super proud of him.

'In general, changes need to take place in the industry around minimum wage levels. We pay as much as we can but it's still never going to be the highest paid job in the world. But as long as there is room in the industry for businesses like ours to keep growing, then there is room for individuals to progress and be promoted within a company and make a career of it.'

www.schlutercoffee.com
E trading@schluter.ch
T +44 (0)151 498 6500

SCHLUTER

SINCE 1858

Speciality green coffee suppliers

since 1858

Purpose.
Passion.
Progress.

STOP.
COLLABORATE
AND LISTEN

In the pursuit of caffeine-spiked sponge, creamy coffee stout and bean-steeped gin, speciality roasters and bean alchemists are creatively collaborating with other artisan businesses. We explore some of the indie outfits fuelling our unconventional caffeine kicks

CRAFT COFFEE

Wickedly smooth, indulgently creamy and concealing a caffeinated kick – coffee stouts have been riding high on the dark stuff's resurgence, with every craft brewery in town bringing out a bean-brewed hybrid.

'With so many parallels between the brewing and roasting industries, it was inevitable that we'd collaborate to create something delicious,' explains Josh Clarke, head of coffee at Clifton Coffee.

'It's a no-brainer as most of the people who care about how coffee is crafted have the same view about their weekend bevvies. As the craft beer revolution is a couple of years ahead of speciality, these partnerships are also introducing great coffee to a new audience.

'We've worked with a number of local breweries who've come to Clifton with an idea for a new brew. Depending on the style of beer and the flavours they're looking to create, we'll match one of our coffees to their vision or go hunting for something else that

works. For Wildebeest, our mash-up with local brewery Wild Beer Co, we picked a fruity, natural Ethiopian which suits the stout's sweet vanilla and cacao characteristics.'

The guys at the Bristol roastery aren't the only ones hopping on the hype. Dorset roaster Finca recently teamed up with local brewery Gyle 59 to create Brad's Coffee Stout after a chance encounter at the Dorchester coffee shop.

'Having recently been converted to coffee by the staff at Finca, it made sense to try combining it with beer,' says Bradley Ware of Gyle 59. Head roaster and Finca owner Don Iszatt knew the bean for the job, selecting a full bodied Agustino Forest coffee with *'caramel and cocoa characteristics packing enough punch for a stout.'*

Carmarthenshire's Coaltown has been at it too, collaborating with Crafty Devil Brewery in Cardiff to produce its amazingly moreish Safe as Milk, which co-owner Scott hopes to stock and serve from the new roastery cafe when it opens in March 2018.

THAT'S THE SPIRIT

I t's not just brews and beers that have been getting cosy. Speciality coffee's also been flirting with the thrills of distillation.

Teaming up with down-the-road distillery Psychopomp, Bristol's Playground Coffee House has co-created the first small batch gin which uses coffee as a botanical.

'The idea came from my quest to create the best espresso martini,' explains Playground's Fabian Dryden. *'After hours of scrolling through Google I couldn't find anyone else who was using coffee to make gin. One of the distillers from Psychopomp is a regular at the coffee shop, so we decided to give it a go.'*

Road testing the speciality spirit in a micro still, the guys hit the sweet spot first time and moved the operation over to the daddy distiller. The heady mix of botanicals in their recipe consists of cascara, peony tea, grapefruit, star anise, juniper and cassia bark, along with whole Kenyan coffee beans from Colonna Coffee in Yate.

'We chose Colonna's Tegu beans as they're packed with exciting fruity flavours to complement the gin's delicate floral fragrance without being too heavy,' adds Fabian.

Grown-up caffeine kicks can be sampled in a range of coffee-infused cocktails or straight up as a G&T at the convivial coffee house on St Nicholas Street. We'd recommend going next level negroni with the cold brew and Playground Gin compilation.

HITTING THE SWEET SPOT

The marriage of coffee and cake is more #couplegoals than Kim and Kanye and, thankfully for us, there's a troop of sweet saviours keeping our quality caffeine and sugar levels topped up in equal measure.

You know that chunk of espresso cheesecake brownie you devoured before your AeroPress reached the table last week? There's a good chance that was made by Cakesmiths – a crack team of Bristol bakers stocking coffee shop counters across the region with killer cakes and next level traybakes.

'We've taken the time to source the best ingredients for our handmade cakes, so it would be madness to back down when it came to the coffee,' explains chief cake pusher, Tom Batlle.

'The Village espresso blend from local roaster Clifton is our go-to for mocha walnut loaf and espresso brownies. Its subtly sweet cocoa and nutty tones add a brilliant flavour to the bakes while, as a slightly darker roast, it holds up against the quality chocolate.'

S30
Perfect Touch

 Wide beverage menu

 Self adjusting grinders

 Bi-directional Wi-Fi control

LaCimbali **S30** is the new superautomatic machine created to offer up to **24 different recipes**. The grouphead design guarantees maximum reliability and consistent beverage quality, while the new milk circuit delivers hot and cold frothed milk directly to the cup.
LaCimbali **S30**, the perfect way to satisfy every taste.

reddot award 2016
winner

 Integral HD Pressure Profiling System
for direct control at any point during the extraction process.

 Touchscreen control
for 'On the fly' pressure profiling and setting control.

 Independent group boilers
for complete temperature control.

 TurboSteam Milk4
for increased productivity and complete milk control.

HOW TO USE THE GUIDE

CAFES

Coffee shops and cafes where you can drink top-notch speciality coffee. We've split the guide into areas to help you find places near you.

ROASTERS

Meet the leading speciality coffee roasters in the South West and South Wales and discover where to source beans to use at home. Find them after the cafes in each area.

MAPS

Every cafe and roastery has a number so you can find them either on the area map at the start of each section, or on the detailed city maps.

MORE GOOD STUFF

Discover MORE GOOD CUPS and MORE GOOD ROASTERS at the back of the book.

Don't forget to let us know how you get on as you explore the best speciality cafes and roasteries.

WWW.INDYCOFFEE.GUIDE

🐦 @indycoffeeguide 📷 @indycoffeeguide

EXPLODING
BAKERY
#74

YOUR
ADVENTURE
STARTS
HERE

SOUTH WALES

LUFKIN
COFFEE
ROASTERS
#5

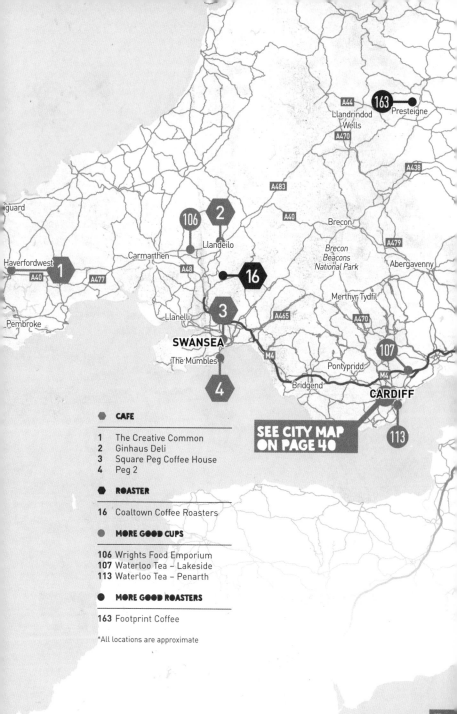

CAFE

1 The Creative Common
2 Ginhaus Deli
3 Square Peg Coffee House
4 Peg 2

ROASTER

16 Coaltown Coffee Roasters

MORE GOOD CUPS

106 Wrights Food Emporium
107 Waterloo Tea – Lakeside
113 Waterloo Tea – Penarth

MORE GOOD ROASTERS

163 Footprint Coffee

*All locations are approximate

SEE CITY MAP ON PAGE 40

CAFE

5 Lufkin Coffee Roasters
6 Brodies Coffee Co
7 200 Degrees
8 The Little Man Coffee Company
9 Hard Lines
10 Corner Coffee
11 The Plan Cafe
12 Uncommon Ground Coffee Roastery
13 Waterloo Tea - Wyndham Arcade
14 Gourmet Coffee Bar & Kitchen
15 Quantum Coffee Roasters

ROASTER

17 Manumit Coffee Roasters
(not shown on map)

MORE GOOD CUPS

108 Waterloo Tea – Penylan
109 The Early Bird
110 KIN+ILK – Pontcanna
111 Hard Lines – Central Market
112 KIN+ILK – Capital Quarter

MORE GOOD ROASTERS

165 Lufkin Coffee Roasters
166 Quantum Coffee Roasters

*All locations are approximate

MAP 1. THE CREATIVE COMMON

The Old Coach House, Goat Street, Haverfordwest, Pembrokeshire, SA61 1PX

Launching as a co-working space in 2015, The Creative Common soon saw an opportunity to caffeinate its population of freelancers and quickly morphed into Haverfordwest's first speciality coffee house.

INSIDER'S TIP ENJOY 15 PER CENT OFF COFFEE HOUSE GOODIES WHEN YOU USE THE CO-WORKING SPACE

Don't be fooled by its rural location – this is no slow-moving bucolic retreat. Make tracks to the thriving coffee shop (the walk up the hill is worth it, promise) and you'll find a buzzing slice of keyboard-tapping, sourdough-munching, idea-bouncing urban life.

Capital Roasters serves the cafe with a killer custom house blend, and owners Mat and Nik are keen to share their passion for speciality: *'Coffee culture is pretty new to our neck of the woods, so we like to think we're among the forerunners of good coffee here.'*

The pair also make regular UK tours to sample new beans, so customers benefit from a supply of fresh finds, as well as the opportunity to pick up coffee related offerings such as the Brew Bar scrub soap made with The Common's recycled coffee grounds.

ESTABLISHED
2016

KEY ROASTER
Capital Roasters

BREWING METHOD
Espresso, V60, cafetiere, Chemex, Clever Dripper, AeroPress

MACHINE
Fracino Bambino

GRINDER
Fracino

OPENING HOURS
Tue-Fri
8am-3pm
Sat 9am-3pm
(extended hours in summer)

 Gluten FREE

 BEANS AVAILABLE INSTORE

 ALTERNATIVE MILK

 WIFI

 CYCLE FRIENDLY

 OUTDOOR seating

 FAMILY FRIENDLY

www.thecreativecommon.co.uk   T: 01437 779397

f The Creative Common   🐦 @coworkpembs   📷 @coworkpembs

MAP №2. GINHAUS DELI

1 Market Street, Llandeilo, Carmarthenshire, SA19 6AH

You don't have to be a gin (or coffee) fan to visit Ginhaus Deli, but it certainly helps. Because with over 410 gins from across the globe, Mike and Kate Kindred and team are certainly doing the juniper plant justice.

Then there's the coffee, sourced from Coaltown Coffee Roasters down the road and served with the skill and care that runs throughout the enterprise.

INSIDER'S TIP THE TEAM ARE NOW SERVING FRED COLD BREW FROM BARCELONA

The pair have turned this old pub into a treasure trove of good eating and drinking with a groaning deli counter of local cheeses and continental meats (the goodies turn up on platters for customers to wolf down at wine barrel tables), gin display and coffee bar. *'We were inspired by a place we visited in Italy,'* says Mike.

With gourmet pizzas on Friday and Saturday nights, monthly gin tasting boards and the introduction of V60s, it's no surprise to discover that Ginhaus is where Mike and Kate go on their night off.

ESTABLISHED
2014

KEY ROASTER
Coaltown Coffee Roasters

BREWING METHOD
Espresso, V60, cold brew

MACHINE
La Spaziale S5 EKTA

GRINDER
Anfim Milano, Mahlkonig Vario

OPENING HOURS
Mon-Thu
8am-5pm
Fri-Sat
8am-10pm

---

www.ginhaus.co.uk   T: 01558 823030

f Ginhaus Deli   🐦 @ginhausdeli   📷 @ginhaus1

MAP № 3. SQUARE PEG COFFEE HOUSE

29b Gower Road, Sketty, Swansea, SA2 9BX

What would it look like if society was one big family? Square Peg wants to find out, starting with a cafe culture revolution. Chucking conformity aside, the word on the street (or in the cafe) is 'different': *'Different is better. Different is new and exciting. We want to make the rules, not stick to them,'* enthuses founder Matt.

The thriving social enterprise gives away its profits to local and international charities (*'We just love giving away money!'*), uses small businesses as suppliers and promotes local artists and musicians: *'We think the small decisions in how we do business and who we source from make a big difference,'* says Matt.

INSIDER'S TIP CHECK OUT FOUNDER MATT'S TEDX TALK ABOUT DOING BUSINESS DIFFERENTLY

And the coffee? Happily, you can expect a cracking cup. Ever-reliable Clifton takes the driving seat in the hopper, with The Barn, Square Mile and Bailies making guest appearances in various espresso and filter guises.

Add to that a glorious all-day brunch menu (try the mushrooms and pickled red cabbage on sourdough), fab music and arts events and you'll soon find yourself in the fold as a fully fledged member of the Peg posse.

ESTABLISHED
2015

KEY ROASTER
Clifton Coffee Roasters, The Barn

BREWING METHOD
Espresso, batch brew, V60, cold brew

MACHINE
La Marzocco Linea PB

GRINDER
Mythos One

OPENING HOURS
Mon-Fri
8am-6.30pm
Sat 8am-5pm

Gluten FREE

BEANS AVAILABLE / INSTORE

ALTERNATIVE MILK

WIFI

CYCLE FRIENDLY

OUTDOOR seating

FAMILY friendly

DISABLED ACCESS

COFFEE COURSES

---

www.squarepeg.org.uk   T: 01792 206593

f Square Peg Coffee   🐦 @squarepegcoffee   📷 @squarepegcoffee

MAP №4. PEG 2

646 Mumbles Road, Mumbles, Swansea, SA3 4EA

Having brewed up a solid following at the original cafe in Sketty, it was a rollercoaster crowdfunding ride that allowed the team at Square Peg to fund a second speciality spot.

A lick of paint, a few reclaimed tables and a couple of quirky collaborations later and the cooperative venture is serving a comprehensive range of coffees from its new Mumbles home, while profits are pumped back into the local community.

INSIDER'S TIP DEVELOPMENTS ARE AFOOT: LOOK OUT FOR NEW FILTER AND BRUNCH OPTIONS

For its Peg-ers, coffee is a conduit to building relationships: *'We want to provide a place where people can feel at home and be able to connect face to face rather than through a phone screen. Our customers are our friends and our staff are our family,'* enthuses barista Josh Pike.

Naturally, these relationships are built on first-class coffee foundations; Bristol roaster Clifton stocks the shop with a stonking blend for espresso while at the filter bar there's a host of single origins to sample.

ESTABLISHED
2017

KEY ROASTER
Clifton Coffee Roasters

BREWING METHOD
Espresso, V60, AeroPress, batch brew, cold brew

MACHINE
La Marzocco Linea

GRINDER
Mythos One, Baratza Encore

OPENING HOURS
Mon–Sat
9am–4pm (seasonal opening hours)

Gluten FREE

BEANS AVAILABLE INSTORE

ALTERNATIVE MILK

WIFI

CYCLE FRIENDLY

FAMILY friendly

DISABLED ACCESS

COFFEE COURSES

---

www.squarepeg.org.uk   T: 01792 360500

f Peg 2 Mumbles   🐦 @squarepegcoffee   📷 @squarepegcoffee

№5. LUFKIN COFFEE ROASTERS

Kings Road Yard, 183a Kings Road, Cardiff, CF11 9DF

There are plenty of places to grab a coffee to-go in Cardiff, but to relish a truly specialist experience it's worth venturing a little further from the city centre.

Lufkin's flower-thronged courtyard in Pontcanna is one such place, where time-rich filter fans can watch beans roasting in the Dätgen drum roaster while sipping single origin pourovers from handmade ceramic mugs.

'Nothing is rushed here,' explain owners Dan and Frances. 'We take great care to slow down. Coffee allows people to step aside from their everyday comings and goings to take a moment.'

This daily ritual is celebrated with a specialist selection of single origins which are roasted on site.

INSIDER'S TIP PAIR YOUR COFFEE WITH ONE OF THE LOCALLY-BAKED SOURDOUGH TOASTS

'Our goal is to provide really good coffee that does justice to the hands that have helped the bean on its journey from cherry to cup,' adds Frances.

If the opportunity doesn't arise to catch glimpses of sunshine from the hand-built terrace, there are a few cosy nooks inside where you can pair your coffee with a topped toast from the well-crafted menu.

ESTABLISHED
2015

KEY ROASTER
Lufkin Coffee Roasters

BREWING METHOD
Espresso, Kalita Wave, cold brew

MACHINE
La Marzocco Linea PB

GRINDER
Mazzer

OPENING HOURS
Mon-Sat
9.30am-5pm
Sun
9.30am-4pm

Gluten FREE

BEANS AVAILABLE
INSTORE

ALTERNATIVE MILK

WIFI

CYCLE FRIENDLY

OUTDOOR seating

FAMILY FRIENDLY

DISABLED ACCESS

BRING YOUR OWN Cup

COFFEE COURSES

www.lufkincoffee.com   T: 07570 811764
f Lufkin Coffee Roasters   🐦 @lufkincoffee   📷 @lufkincoffee

MAP № 6. BRODIES COFFEE CO

Gorsedd Gardens, Cardiff, CF10 3NP

Secure one of the seats outside Brodies on a sunny day in the 'Diff and you'll be imbibing a brew in what might just be the city's most idyllic spot.

Overlooking the National Museum from its nest in Gorsedd Gardens, the once run-down cabin is now a hive of caffeinated activity, serving curious tourists, flagging families and the neighbouring office force with carefully crafted Coaltown coffee.

Time spent in Wellington, New Zealand inspired the Brodies to sling shots for a living, though, starting out with a roaming cafe in 2012, it was four years of fuelling festival goers and party patrons before they secured a permanent spot.

INSIDER'S TIP THE VEGWARE TAKEOUT CUPS NOT ONLY LOOK FLY, THEY'RE 100 PER CENT COMPOSTABLE

The charming cabin is now a one-stop shop for silky Welsh espresso, freshly stacked baguettes and locally baked cakes. We'd recommend picking up a homemade cold brew and chunk of chocolate peanut butter flapjack or gluten-free brownie for a speciality-grade picnic in front of the fountains.

ESTABLISHED
2016

KEY ROASTER
Coaltown Coffee Roasters

BREWING METHOD
Espresso, cold brew

MACHINE
La Spaziale S2

GRINDER
Sanremo SR70

OPENING HOURS
Mon-Fri
8am-5pm
Sat
10am-5pm
Sun
10am-4pm

www.brodiescoffeeco.com   T: 07414 963591

f Brodies Coffee Co   🐦 @brodiescoffee   📷 @brodies_coffee

MAP № 7. 200 DEGREES

115 Queen Street, Cardiff, CF10 2BH

A fresher on the Cardiff coffee scene, this cafe-roaster-barista-school combo is a sanctuary for aspiring espresso slingers, pourover purists and students seeking caffeinated refuge.

Its name is an introductory lesson in bean baking and refers to the temperature at which master roaster Mike Steele slowly roasts ethically sourced green beans for his *smoother tasting* house coffees. The Brazilian beauties used in the Love Affair blend can be supped in-shop via espresso and filter or hurried home to be brewed on your shiny new Chemex, purchased at the bar.

INSIDER'S TIP: THESE GUYS ARE HOT ON LATTE ART – ASK THEM TO THROW THEIR LATEST SHAPE

A timetable of rotating single origins changes every fortnight and calls for a return trip to sample the newcomers. While a menu of edible delights – bulging baguettes, seasonal salads and diet-disgracing cakes – is updated just as frequently.

Cosy up next to the neon fire at the back of this city centre hangout and stick around for one of the evening socials: the latte art throwdowns are a hit with the barista school's latest graduates.

ESTABLISHED
2017

KEY ROASTER
200 Degrees

BREWING METHOD
Espresso, V60, AeroPress

MACHINE
Victoria Arduino Black Eagle 3 group

GRINDER
Mythos One x 2, MDX On Demand

OPENING HOURS
Mon-Fri
7am-8pm
Sat 8am-7pm
Sun 9.30am-6pm

www.200degs.com T: 02921 320708

f 200 Degrees Coffee Shop, Cardiff 🐦 @200degscardiff 📷 @200degs

MAP №8. THE LITTLE MAN COFFEE COMPANY

Ivor House, Bridge Street, Cardiff, CF10 2EE

Giving over 25 different roasters a go since opening in autumn 2014, this former post office accommodates one of Cardiff's most comprehensive coffee collections.

Now in its fourth year, owner Rob Cooper has introduced a second central location, The Little Man Garage on Tudor Lane, along with a travelling tuk-tuk coffee cart.

At the original cafe, the current stockpile of UK and European beans sits behind a slate-clad bar, along with a range of kit for the burgeoning filter buff. Anything delicious discovered via the brew bar can be purchased and taken home for further investigation, or sipped with fellow coffee folk swapping stories at one of the communal tables.

INSIDER'S TIP DAWN, DAY OR DUSK: HIRE LITTLE MAN FOR YOUR NEXT KNEES-UP OR OFFICE DEBRIEF

Also worth inspecting is the basement kitchen's freshly baked haul. Grab a seat in the downstairs co-working space and get first look – and sniff – of the brownies, lemon drizzle cake and buttery croissants making their way to the counter.

A busy calendar of events means there's often evening entertainment at the sociable hub: look out for gin and Scrabble, coffee cupping and supper clubs.

ESTABLISHED
2014

KEY ROASTER
Round Hill Roastery, Passion Fruit Coffee Roasters, Welsh Coffee Company

BREWING METHOD
Espresso, drip, immersion, cold brew

MACHINE
La Marzocco Linea AV

GRINDER
Compak R80, Compak E8

OPENING HOURS
Mon-Fri
7am-9pm
Sat-Sun 8am-6pm

 Gluten FREE

 BEANS AVAILABLE INSTORE

 ALTERNATIVE MILK

 WIFI

 CYCLE FRIENDLY

 FAMILY FRIENDLY

 DISABLED ACCESS

 BRING YOUR OWN Cup

COFFEE COURSES

www.littlemancoffee.co.uk   T: 07933 844234

f The Little Man Coffee Co   @littlemancoffee   @littlemancoffee

9. HARD LINES

The Castle Emporium, Womanby Street, Cardiff, CF10 1BS

Spinning vinyl and pulling espresso from its patch in The Castle Emporium, Hard Lines provides old school tunes and caffeinated consolation for those escaping Cardiff's crowds.

Working as sound engineers – but moonlighting as full-time coffee fanatics – owners Matt and Soph launched Hard Lines as a pop-up in May 2016 before settling into permanent digs in the indie hub in October the same year.

INSIDER'S TIP
LOOK OUT FOR A SECOND HARD LINES AT CARDIFF CENTRAL MARKET

'In the beginning we just served AeroPress until we saved up enough to buy a La Spaziale machine,' explains Soph.

With an ever-expanding list of roaster favourites, the friends opted to go omni-roaster style with an evolving bill of beans from across the UK and Europe. Extract, Clifton and Neighbourhood make periodic appearances, though single origins from roasters less prevalent in Cardiff (Crankhouse, Pink Lane and Triple Co) often take guest spots.

The coffee shop and record store has also played a part in South Wales's developing coffee culture, hosting cupping events with regional roasters and fuelling album launches with finely crafted filter.

ESTABLISHED
2016

KEY ROASTER
Extract Coffee Roasters, Neighbourhood Coffee, Clifton Coffee Roasters

BREWING METHOD
Espresso, filter, batch brew, cold brew

MACHINE
La Spaziale S5

GRINDER
Mahlkonig K30

OPENING HOURS
Mon-Fri
8am-5pm
Sat 10am-6pm

 Gluten FREE

 BEANS AVAILABLE INSTORE

  ALTERNATIVE MILK

 WIFI

 CYCLE FRIENDLY

 FAMILY FRIENDLY

 DISABLED ACCESS

  BRING YOUR OWN CUP

T: 07428 695997

 f Hard Lines Coffee 🐦 @hardlinescoffee 📷 @hardlinescoffee

MAP 10. CORNER COFFEE

13 High Street, Cardiff, CF10 1AX

As if written in the stars, it was finding an empty space on the corner of Cardiff's High Street Arcade that allowed Chris Corner to transform his pop-up venture into a fully-fledged coffee shop.

The move to a permanent spot in the city centre allowed Chris to work closely with his former colleagues at The Missing Bean in Oxford and develop a bespoke house blend for his new project.

'I got together with the guys to craft a blend unique to Corner Coffee which incorporates beans from Colombia, Ethiopia, Rwanda and Peru,' explains Chris.

INSIDER'S TIP ASK CHRIS FOR HIS HOME BREWING TIPS FOR THE LATEST GUEST SINGLE ORIGIN

Revolving single origins from a number of indies including Crankhouse and Welsh roasters Coaltown and Lufkin join the house blend on the swish Faema machine, with the latest guest roast also available to sample via V60 or bagged up for home brewing.

With a light-flooded glass frontage, pared-back design and a welcoming gaggle of baristas, Corner Coffee is a lovely spot in which to linger. Take up residence at one of the window stools, order a V60 and a goat's cheese, fig chutney and tomato-filled sourdough sarnie and soak up the vibe.

ESTABLISHED
2017

KEY ROASTER
The Missing Bean

BREWING METHOD
Espresso, V60

MACHINE
Faema E71

GRINDER
Mahlkonig Twin Air

OPENING HOURS
Mon-Fri
7.30am-6pm
Sat 8.30am-6pm
Sun 10am-5pm

T: 02921 320400
 Corner Coffee @cornercoffee_co @cornercoffee_co

MAP 11. THE PLAN CAFE

28-29 Morgan Arcade, Cardiff, CF10 1AF

Head to this sunny coffee shop in Morgan Arcade when the clouds part and you'll be in the right place to discover one of South Wales' finest cold brews.

Seasoned barista Trevor Hyam has been working on his recipe for years, double-filtering James Gourmet single origin beans overnight for a refreshingly fruity summertime hit.

In addition, Trevor pours love into each cappuccino, americano and piccolo served at this glass-panelled spot, and shares his skills with The Plan's legion of baristas who benefit from daily on-the-job training.

INSIDER'S TIP CHECK OUT THE LATEST SEASONAL SINGLE ORIGIN ON FRENCH PRESS

Choose a ground-floor window spot or the more secluded mezzanine to peruse the menu. Welsh classics such as proper rarebit with poached eggs offer a delicious start to the day, while freshly prepared lunch plates prove a perfect pairing with the Ross-on-Wye roasted coffee.

Loyal regulars and curious tourists spill out from the busy cafe onto a cluster of tables under the Victorian arcade, and four-legged friends are welcome to join in for mid-afternoon munchies.

ESTABLISHED
2002

KEY ROASTER
James Gourmet
Coffee

BREWING METHOD
Espresso,
french press,
batch brew,
cold brew

MACHINE
Astoria Plus
4 You

GRINDER
Anfim Super
Caimano

OPENING HOURS
Mon-Sat
8.45am-5pm
Sun
9.30am-4pm

---

www.theplancafecardiff.co.uk　T: 02920 398764

f The Plan Café Cardiff　🐦 @theplancafe

MAP 12. UNCOMMON GROUND COFFEE ROASTERY

10-12 Royal Arcade, Cardiff, CF10 1AE

When we last caught up with Ian and Paul Hayman of Uncommon Ground, they were itching to get their roastery started.

A year down the line, the brothers have achieved their dream, and Uncommon Ground now stocks its grinders with its own Cardiff-roasted speciality beans and its chillers with homemade cold brew.

INSIDER'S TIP THE REUBEN RYE SANDWICH AND SIGNATURE FLAT WHITE ARE A CLASSIC COMBO

The original plan was to roast at the back of their shop in the historic Royal Arcade, but the boys opted instead for a site on the edge of the city, where they've thrown everything into creating their perfect house espresso and a selection of single origins for filter.

The elegant, glass fronted shop has loads of room where customers can chill out while sampling the house speciality. Bare brick and feature lighting create an appealing space in which to catch up with friends and colleagues – or your emails (boo).

And while the roastery currently only supplies the coffee house and wholesale customers, keep an eye open for future plans to sell beans online.

ESTABLISHED
2015

KEY ROASTER
Uncommon Ground

BREWING METHOD
Espresso, V60, cold brew, AeroPress

MACHINE
La Spaziale

GRINDER
Anfim Caimano OD

OPENING HOURS
Mon-Sat
7.30am-6.30pm
Sun
10am-5.30pm

Gluten FREE

BEANS AVAILABLE INSTORE

ALTERNATIVE MILK

WIFI

OUTDOOR SEATING

FAMILY FRIENDLY

COFFEE COURSES

---

www.uncommon-ground.co.uk

f Uncommon Ground Coffee Roastery 🐦 @_uncommonground 📷 @_uncommonground

MAP 13. WATERLOO TEA – WYNDHAM ARCADE

21-25 Wyndham Arcade, The Hayes, Cardiff, CF10 1FH

Cafe habitué across the UK know this loose-leaf tea trader for its artisan collection of infusions but it's also a trailblazer for speciality coffee on its home turf in South Wales.

Its third tea house – there are others in Roath and Penarth, along with the original in Penylan – is to be discovered in the city centre's beautiful, Edwardian Wyndham Arcade.

A favourite with Cardiff's brunchers and cake fans, the cafe showcases guest beans from a range of European roasters such as Round Hill and Wendelboe alongside the house coffees by Yallah and Has Bean.

INSIDER'S TIP CHOOSE FROM OVER 50 LOOSE-LEAF TEAS BREWED TO PERFECTION ON FOUR MULTI-TEMP BOILERS

The drinks list reads like an encyclopedia of fine teas and carefully crafted coffees. Get the party started with a house speciality tea, then follow with something from the homemade brunch menu and an accompanying coffee flight: a palate cleansing cascara, single shot 5oz cappuccino and an espresso, served on a wooden board.

Known for throwing a good knees up, Waterloo has hosted the Welsh AeroPress Championships, UK Brewers Cup and Tea Brewers Cup, along with an eclectic line-up of supper clubs and events.

ESTABLISHED
2014

KEY ROASTER
Yallah Coffee,
Has Bean Coffee

BREWING METHOD
Espresso,
Kalita Wave,
V60, AeroPress,
cold brew

MACHINE
La Marzocco
FB80

GRINDER
Mythos,
Mahlkonig EK 43

OPENING HOURS
Mon-Fri
8.30am-5pm
Sat 8.30am-6pm
Sun 9.30am-5pm

Gluten FREE

BEANS AVAILABLE / INSTORE

ALTERNATIVE MILK

WIFI

CYCLE FRIENDLY

OUTDOOR seating

FAMILY friendly

DISABLED ACCESS

COFFEE COURSES

www.waterlootea.com T: 02920 376249

f Waterloo Tea   🐦 @waterlootea   📷 @waterlootea

MAP 14. GOURMET COFFEE BAR & KITCHEN

Central Square, Cardiff, CF10 1EP

Summoning caffeine-starved commuters with the word 'coffee' illuminated in lights, Gourmet Coffee Bar ensures day trippers fresh off the train at Cardiff Central don't have any trouble finding their first fix.

Neatly tucked into a corner of the art deco station, the compact cafe's clan of chipper baristas have crafted speciality coffee at this busy thoroughfare since April 2016.

INSIDER'S TIP BRING A KEEPCUP FOR A DISCOUNT ON YOUR FAVOURITE BREW

Winning-over former syrup sinners and chain conformists with Union's darkly indulgent Revelation blend on espresso – think rich treacle notes with dark chocolate and cinnamon – manager Jason Brough has introduced a filter from the London roaster this year which offers fruitier cherry, macadamia and milk chocolate flavours.

'We've got Bobolink on batch brew and it's going down a treat with the rush-hour regulars,' says Jason.

It's not just train hoppers who swing by for a cortado-to-go; flagging shoppers and local office workers also flock to the glossy glass bar for its velvety flat whites and a chunk of something chocolatey.

ESTABLISHED
2016

KEY ROASTER
Union Hand-Roasted Coffee

BREWING METHOD
Espresso, batch brew

MACHINE
La Marzocco Linea Classic

GRINDER
Mahlkonig K30

OPENING HOURS
Mon-Fri
6am-7pm
Sat 7am-7pm
Sun 7.30am-3pm

www.gourmetcoffeebar.co.uk   T: 07399 546206

f Gourmet Coffee Bar & Kitchen   🐦 @gourmetcbandk   📷 @gourmetcoffeebar

15. QUANTUM COFFEE ROASTERS

58 Bute Street, Quayside, Cardiff, CF10 5BN

Greek coffee isn't your usual third wave offering, yet when Dimitri and Katia opened their roastery/cafe hybrid in 2015, the duo were keen to honour their Hellenic heritage.

There's quite the choice for the coffee connoisseur at this spacious corner spot on Cardiff Bay. The troop of traditional Greek, Turkish and Arabic coffees sits alongside Quantum's selection of house-roasted blends and single origins, while an impressive collection of brewing gear offers options aplenty for your pick.

INSIDER'S TIP
ON THE COFFEE ALE HYPE? CHECK OUT QUANTUM'S COLD BREW COLLABORATION WITH MAD DOG BREWING CO.

The interior echoes Dimitri and Katia's passion for the science and craftsmanship of coffee, blending experimental cold brew towers and roasting paraphernalia with vintage furniture and original photography.

If you can, nab a spot on the leather Chesterfield to sample the slow-drip cold brew coffee. There's also organic porridge and freshly grilled sandwiches to feed awakening appetites, as well as locally baked cakes and traybakes for afternoon gratification.

ESTABLISHED
2015

KEY ROASTER
Quantum Coffee Roasters

BREWING METHOD
Espresso, V60, Chemex, cold brew tower, ibrick

MACHINE
Britesso

GRINDER
Iberital, Santos, Zaras

OPENING HOURS
Mon-Fri
8am-6pm
Sat 9am-6pm
Sun 10am-6pm
(extended hours in summer)

 Gluten FREE

 BEANS AVAILABLE INSTORE

 ALTERNATIVE MILK

 WIFI

 FAMILY FRIENDLY

 DISABLED ACCESS

---

www.quantumroasters.co.uk   T: 07413 543335

f Quantum Coffee Roasters   🐦 @quantumroasters   📷 @quantumroasters

ROASTERS

SOUTH WALES

MAP № 16. COALTOWN COFFEE ROASTERS
Foundry Road, Ammanford, Carmarthenshire, SA18 2LS

Three years after launching their coffee roasting business, Gordon and Scott James of Coaltown are revving up once again for their next adventure: the launch of their new roastery cafe and academy.

Based in the ex-mining community of Ammanford in Carmarthenshire, the pair introduced the concept of roasting 'black gold' as an alternative to mining anthracite.

Starting off small and cooking up beans on Gordon's homemade roaster in the garage, they've outgrown their nifty set up and now need a load more room for the chunky 75kg Probat and all those bags of greens.

'THE NEW PROJECT WILL INCLUDE THE COALTOWN ACADEMY'

The new project, which will open in March 2018 on Foundry Road, will include the Coaltown Academy to help grow local employment through coffee, as well as roastery tours and an in-house cafe. Although, of course, you'll still be able to get your hands on a Coaltown coffee at lots of nearby cafes and foodie establishments.

Other news this year is the pair's plan to start sourcing some coffee direct – more pith helmet than pit head ...

ESTABLISHED
2014

ROASTER
MAKE & SIZE
Probat UG75 75kg,
Probatone 12 12kg

OPEN
BY APPOINTMENT

COFFEE
COURSES

BEANS
AVAILABLE
ONSITE

ONLINE

---

www.coaltowncoffee.co.uk   T: 01269 400105

f Coaltown Coffee Roasters   🐦 @coaltowncoffee   📷 @coaltowncoffee

17. MANUMIT COFFEE ROASTERS

Cardiff

A translation of 'release from slavery; set free' in Middle English, Manumit works with survivors of modern slavery to roast speciality coffee in the heart of South Wales.

Dai – the pastor behind the project – was tasked with finding a platform from which to help people who'd been rescued from human trafficking to rebuild their lives. The result saw him firing up a 1950s Probat roaster in June 2017.

'We chose coffee because speciality is an international phenomenon,' he explains. *'We've teamed up with the SCA to train survivors as both baristas and roasters, with the hope that wherever they relocate, they'll be able to draw on their new skills.'*

Although a dedicated coffee drinker, Dai's background in charity work didn't give him much relevant experience when it came to his new role as head roaster. *'There's been a lot of learning on the job,'* he admits, *'but we wouldn't be where we are now without the support and guidance of some of the region's finest roasters'.*

Currently stocking Manumit's online shop and a cluster of cafes with a seasonal house roast, all profits go direct to anti-slavery projects. The next task for the team is a range of single origins named after the two survivors who have been roasting with Dai since day one.

ESTABLISHED
2017

ROASTER
MAKE & SIZE
1950s Probat
LG5 5kg

COURSES

BEANS
AVAILABLE
ONLINE

www.manumitcoffee.co.uk   T: 07481 106046

f Manumit Coffee Roasters   🐦 @manumitcoffee   📷 @manumitcoffee

GLOUCES-TERSHIRE

THE COFFEE
DISPENSARY
#19

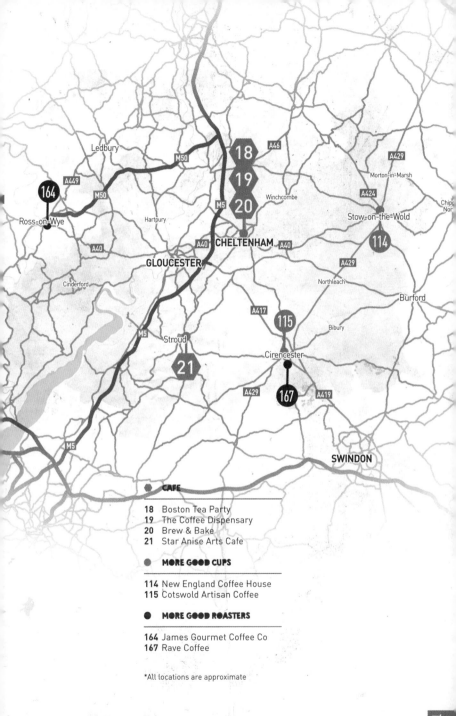

CAFE

18 Boston Tea Party
19 The Coffee Dispensary
20 Brew & Bake
21 Star Anise Arts Cafe

MORE GOOD CUPS

114 New England Coffee House
115 Cotswold Artisan Coffee

MORE GOOD ROASTERS

164 James Gourmet Coffee Co
167 Rave Coffee

*All locations are approximate

MAP № 18. BOSTON TEA PARTY – CHELTENHAM

45-49 Clarence Street, Cheltenham, Gloucestershire, GL50 3JS

Claiming a prime spot on historic Clarence Street is Cheltenham's chapter of BTP.

Although it's one of the largest in the group – there's space for 160 coffee-loving locals – you'll want to get to this popular spot early to grab a window seat. Alternatively, snuggle up on a corner sofa and while away the hours with a good read.

Once you've drooled over the piled-high bakes and brilliant brunch offerings, choose your poison from the espresso menu. Delivering phenomenal coffee is part and parcel of any BTP experience, and this one is no exception.

INSIDER'S TIP GET A SUNSHINE FIX ON WARMER DAYS WHEN THE CONCERTINA DOORS ARE FLUNG OPEN

Sublime South American beans from mainstay roaster Extract are partnered with a seasonally changing array of filters. And the crew are all about providing the perfect cup without turned-up noses – coffee rookies are welcomed with open arms.

Ethics are top of the priority list: *'We care about the impact we make on the planet, and try to do things in a better, greener way – from energy consumption and ingredient sourcing to what we do with waste.'*

ESTABLISHED
2014

KEY ROASTER
Extract Coffee Roasters

BREWING METHOD
Espresso, filter

MACHINE
La Marzocco PB

GRINDER
Mazzer Major

OPENING HOURS
Mon-Sat
7am-8pm
Sun
7am-7pm

---

www.bostonteaparty.co.uk   T: 01242 573935

f Boston Tea Party Cafés 🐦 @btpcafes 📷 @btpcafes

MAP 19. THE COFFEE DISPENSARY

18 Regent Street, Cheltenham, Gloucestershire, GL50 1HE

Wade past central Cheltenham's corporate coffee chains to discover an indie sanctum of speciality on Regent Street.

Dealing in exotic single origins, cracking cold brew and whatever else owner Gary Marshall can get his hands on, The Coffee Dispensary celebrates the wonderfully geeky side of the classic caffeine hit.

South West roasters such as Extract, Colonna and Clifton feature on a filter board that's a veritable tour of caffeinated Britain, so there's always something new to sample via V60, AeroPress or syphon.

INSIDER'S TIP LOOK OUT FOR REGULAR CUPPINGS, COFFEE TALKS AND LIVE MUSIC EVENTS

Groaning shelves of beans, brewing kit and coffee paraphernalia also enable visitors to recreate the science of speciality at home.

If you're settling in with a bean brew or a Blue Bird fruit tea at the contemporary townhouse, make sure to treat yourself to an accompanying morsel such as an award winning brownie from Hetty's Tea Party or a pastry from Baker of the Year, Salt Bakehouse.

ESTABLISHED
2015

KEY ROASTER
Extract Coffee Roasters

BREWING METHOD
Espresso, V60, AeroPress, syphon

MACHINE
Sanremo Opera

GRINDER
Mahlkonig K30, Mahlkonig EK 43

OPENING HOURS
Mon-Sat
8.30am-5.30pm
Sun
10am-4.30pm

Gluten FREE

BEANS AVAILABLE INSTORE

ALTERNATIVE MILK

WIFI

CYCLE FRIENDLY

OUTDOOR seating

COFFEE COURSES

---

www.the-coffee-dispensary.co.uk   T: 01242 260597

f The Coffee Dispensary   🐦 @coffeedispenser   📷 @the_coffee_dispensary

№20. BREW & BAKE

217 Bath Road, Cheltenham, Gloucestershire, GL53 7NA

For kid-in-a-sweet-shop delights of the coffee and cake variety, make a greedy break from the centre of Cheltenham for the dough-tastic embrace of Brew & Bake.

Crafting up to ten showstopping bakes to bedeck the wood-clad bar each day, the team at Brew & Bake ensure that all good intentions are left firmly at the door. Expertly pulled espresso entices visitors to stay long enough to justify a second slice.

INSIDER'S TIP LOOK OUT FOR THE LINE-UP OF REGULAR POP-UP SUPPER CLUBS

Whatever sweet or savoury sensation you succumb to (we recommend a chunk of the mango and coconut cake and the artisan sausage rolls), a menu of expertly-roasted coffees and a library of filter options offer a speciality pairing to your pick. Look out for guest beans from some of the country's top roasters alongside the single origin from UE.

The drool-inducing brunch and lunch menus are another highlight at this contemporary coffee shop. Vegan pancakes with maple-roasted nuts and fruit compote and the n'duja scotch egg taste as good as they'll look on your Instagram.

ESTABLISHED
2015

KEY ROASTER
UE Coffee Roasters

BREWING METHOD
Espresso, V60, Chemex, AeroPress

MACHINE
La Marzocco Classic

GRINDER
Super Jolly on demand

OPENING HOURS
Mon-Sat
7am-4pm
Sun
9am-4pm

---

www.brewandbake.coffee T: 01242 580875

f Brew & Bake 🐦 @brewandbakehq 📷 @brewandbake_hq

MAP№ 21. STAR ANISE ARTS CAFE

1 Gloucester Street, Stroud, Gloucestershire, GL5 1QG

With a lively schedule of art, music, poetry, theatre and storytelling events keeping the gorgeous grub and quality coffee company, a trip to community conscious Star Anise provides nourishment for both mind and body.

For appetites in need of satiating, there's a wholefood menu thriving with fish, veggie and vegan fodder. Those looking for a healthy hot-lunch hit can't go wrong with a vibrant buddha bowl or gently spiced pakoras, while carb-chasers can rely on the irresistible daily offering of homemade pastries, cakes and bread.

INSIDER'S TIP HONE YOUR SOURDOUGH SKILLS AT THE REGULAR BREADMAKING WORKSHOPS

Caffeinated comfort comes from roaster of choice, Extract. The team favour its Original Espresso, while the Swiss Water blend provides a naturally decaffeinated alternative.

Pencil the last Friday of each month into the diary for night-time nourishment at the supper club, where toe-tapping live music is accompanied by guest chef appearances.

ESTABLISHED
2004

KEY ROASTER
Extract Coffee
Roasters

BREWING METHOD
Espresso

MACHINE
Sanremo

GRINDER
Sanremo,
Mythos One

OPENING HOURS
Mon-Fri
8.30am-5pm
Sat
8.30am-4.30pm

Gluten FREE

BEANS AVAILABLE
INSTORE

ALTERNATIVE
MILK

WIFI

CYCLE
FRIENDLY

OUTDOOR
seating

FAMILY
FRIENDLY

DISABLED
ACCESS

www.staraniseartscafe.com   T: 01453 840021

f Star Anise Arts Cafe   🐦 @staranisecafe   📷 @staranisecafe

BRISTOL

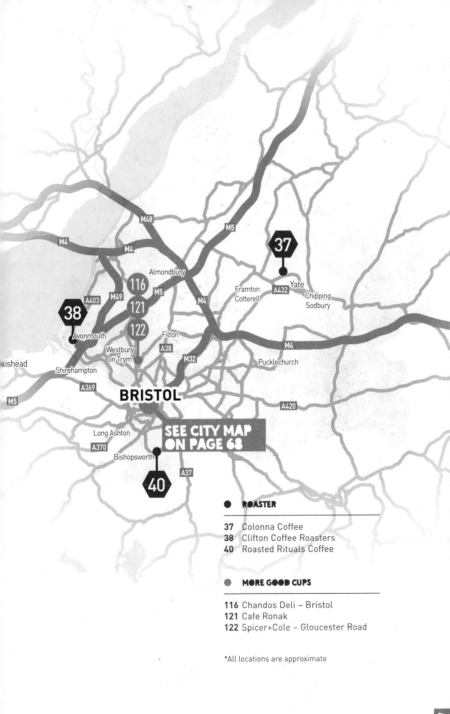

SEE CITY MAP ON PAGE 68

● **ROASTER**

37 Colonna Coffee
38 Clifton Coffee Roasters
40 Roasted Rituals Coffee

● **MORE GOOD CUPS**

116 Chandos Deli – Bristol
121 Cafe Ronak
122 Spicer+Cole – Gloucester Road

*All locations are approximate

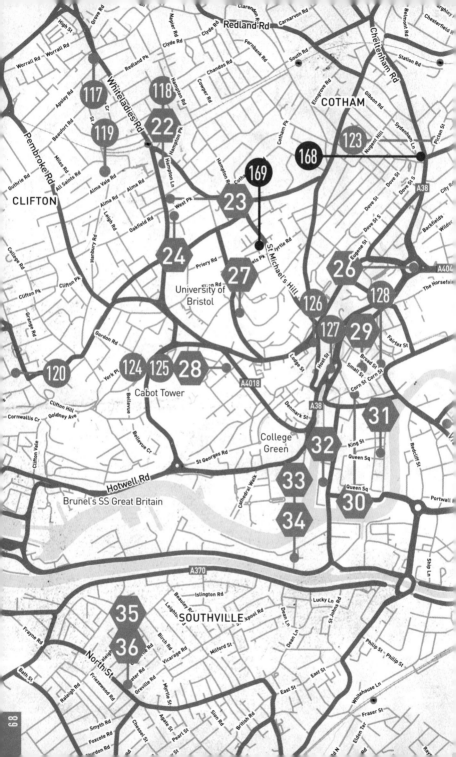

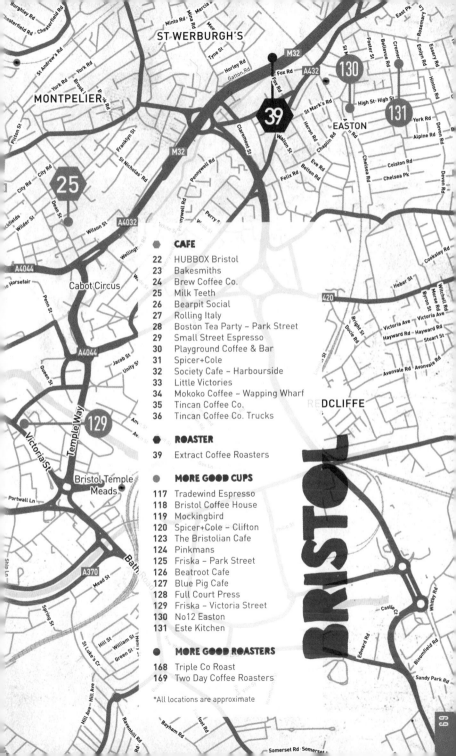

● CAFE

● ROASTER

● MORE GOOD CUPS

● MORE GOOD ROASTERS

*All locations are approximate

№22. HUBBOX BRISTOL

113 Whiteladies Road, Clifton, Bristol, BS8 2PB

Move over biscotti, step aside stuffed doughnuts: coffee's found a new greedy partner at Bristol's latest foodie opening.

Dealing in burgers, craft beers and banging brews, Hubbox started life as an offshoot of the original Hub in St Ives before snaking its award winning burger bars across Cornwall and Devon to Clifton.

The sixth set-up honours Hubbox's Cornish roots with espresso from Origin Coffee. The Helston-based roastery not only stocks the hopper with its Pathfinder blend but also whips Hubbox's band of baristas into shape so they can fashion flawless flatties.

INSIDER'S TIP CHECK OUT THE COLLECTION OF CORNISH CRAFT BEERS

Greedy revellers will be happy to know that this easygoing eatery is an all-day affair. Kickstart the fun with a double shot macchiato before diving face first into one of the piled-high patties (we recommend the Pit Burger – 6oz beef patty, slow-smoked beef brisket, barbecue sauce, American burger cheese and 'slaw). Then fill the afternoon with a speciality mocha and a chunk of locally crafted cake, followed by a post 5pm espresso martini.

ESTABLISHED
2017

KEY ROASTER
Origin Coffee
Roasters

BREWING METHOD
Espresso

MACHINE
La Marzocco
Strada custom

GRINDER
Nuova Simonelli
Mythos One

OPENING HOURS
Mon-Sun
10am-10pm

WIFI

OUTDOOR SEATING

FAMILY FRIENDLY

DISABLED ACCESS

---

www.hubbox.co.uk   T: 01179 731090
f Hubbox   🐦 @hubbox_bris   📷 @hubbox_

23. BAKESMITHS

65 Whiteladies Road, Clifton, Bristol, BS8 2LY

Seasoned cafe clientele will have encountered Cakesmiths' colourful compilation of enticing traybakes and wickedly gooey brownies at coffee houses across the country. But for doughy gratification still steaming from the oven, a pilgrimage to its HQ in Bristol is a must.

INSIDER'S TIP
BOOK INTO CAKE SCHOOL AND NAIL BAKED BEAUTIES SUCH AS THE ULTIMATE BROWNIE

Churning out chewy sourdough loaves, chocolate-studded banana bread and sweet masterpieces that would make Mary Berry proud, its contemporary bakery on the corner of Whiteladies Road is a cathedral to carbs 'n' coffee.

The latter is supplied by Clifton, which stocks the bakehouse with its carefully roasted beans for espresso and filter. The local roaster also provides the caffeinated goods for Cakesmiths faves such as a drool-inducing espresso cheesecake brownie and moreish mocha walnut loaf.

It's not just sweet thrills and caffeinated kicks the guys are supplying, either. A brunch and lunch menu (with vegan options) of topped toasts, brekkie-stuffed brioche buns and hot pressed sarnies is greedily good.

ESTABLISHED
2016

KEY ROASTER
Clifton Coffee Roasters

BREWING METHOD
Espresso, filter

MACHINE
La Marzocco Linea

GRINDER
Compak E8

OPENING HOURS
Mon-Fri 8am-5pm
Sat 9am-5pm
Sun 10am-4pm

 Gluten FREE
 BEANS AVAILABLE INSTORE
 ALTERNATIVE MILK
 WIFI
 OUTDOOR seating
 FAMILY FRIENDLY
BRING YOUR OWN Cup

www.bakesmiths.co.uk   T: 01179 735644

f Bakesmiths   🐦 @bakesmithshq   📷 @bakesmiths_hq

№24. BREW COFFEE CO.

45 Whiteladies Road, Clifton, Bristol, BS8 2LS

The yellow seats outside Brew are a beacon of brightly coloured hope for caffeine cravers from all corners of the speciality-inspired city, luring them into the Whiteladies Road cafe for a sure-fire shot.

And boy does it deliver. Cranking out great coffee with a side of lip-smackingly scrummy food, Brew has Bristol wrapped around its little finger.

Teaming up with local roaster Clifton Coffee, the guys specialise in single origin filters via pourover, with the La Marzocco Linea machine on standby for those who favour espresso. Beans from other South West stalwarts such as Crankhouse and Round Hill are to be found on the rotating guest menu too.

INSIDER'S TIP CHECK OUT THE YELLOW PLANTERS WHILE YOU SUP ALFRESCO – THE HERBS ARE USED IN THE KITCHEN

If you're ravenous for avo toast or starving for sourdough, sate your appetite with antipodean-style brekkies, seasonal brunch plates and Middle Eastern-inspired lunches.

And we're all over this year's new menu addition: Brew-made sausage burgers with 'shroom ketchup, aioli and leaves.

ESTABLISHED
2014

KEY ROASTER
Clifton Coffee Roasters

BREWING METHOD
Espresso, pourover

MACHINE
La Marzocco Linea PB

GRINDER
Nuova Simonelli Mythos One

OPENING HOURS
Mon-Fri
7.30am-6pm
Sat 8am-6pm
Sun 9am-5pm

Gluten FREE
BEANS AVAILABLE INSTORE
ALTERNATIVE MILK
WIFI
CYCLE FRIENDLY
FAMILY FRIENDLY
DISABLED ACCESS
BRING YOUR OWN Cup

---

www.brewcoffeecompany.co.uk   T: 01179 732842
f Brew Coffee Company   🐦 @brewcc   📷 @brewcc

MAP25. MILK TEETH

21 Portland Square, Bristol, BS2 8SJ

Whether you're after chewy sourdough, fiery chilli oil or carefully roasted beans, you're never far from an artisan producer in Bristol. And at Milk Teeth, the city's latest indie opening, Josh Bowker is proudly curating local produce alongside some stonking speciality coffee.

INSIDER'S TIP
CLEAR AN HOUR FOR YOUR TRIP AS THE CRACKING PLAYLIST IS WORTH STICKING AROUND FOR

Part cafe, part pantry, part cool place to hang out, the Portland Square venue is a one-stop-shop for Bristol-made beauties including fruit-laden jams, loose-leaf tea, urban honey and an expertly pulled Extract espresso.

Fellow Bristolian roasters such as Clifton, Roasted Rituals and Triple Co enjoy stints on the guest filter, providing an ample opportunity to sample something new via V60.

Visit for the coffee, stay for the waffles: the vegan bad boys are the star of the foodie offering and give the peanut butter brownies and Farro Bakery croissants a run for their money – try 'em smothered in maple syrup and topped with nuts.

ESTABLISHED
2017

KEY ROASTER
Extract Coffee Roasters

BREWING METHOD
Espresso, V60, Marco batch brew

MACHINE
Sanremo Zoe

GRINDER
Victoria Arduino Mythos One, Wilfa Svart

OPENING HOURS
Mon-Fri
7am-8pm
Sat-Sun
9am-8pm

 Gluten FREE

 BEANS AVAILABLE INSTORE

 ALTERNATIVE MILK

 WIFI

 CYCLE FRIENDLY

 OUTDOOR SEATING

 FAMILY FRIENDLY

BRING YOUR OWN Cup.

www.milkteethportlandsq.co.uk   T: 01179 426868

f Milk Teeth Café & Stores   🐦 @milkteethcafe   📷 @milkteethportlandsq

26. BEARPIT SOCIAL

Unit 1, St James Barton Roundabout (The Bearpit), Bristol, BS1 3LE

Inspired to change the world one cup of coffee at a time, Miriam Delogu opened her unique shipping container cafe in the city centre in 2013.

Seeking to create a safe and welcoming destination where once only beer-ed up drunks hung out, the Bearpit Bristol CIC was created in 2017 to inspire the city to further reclaim the former roundabout. The neglected space now bustles with commuters sipping from KeepCups, skaters honing 360s and shoppers stocking up on fresh fruit and veggies.

With a diverse community finding caffeinated refuge at this social hub, the team serve seasonal, ethically sourced, single origin beans from the city's Wogan Coffee as both espresso based drinks and filter brews.

INSIDER'S TIP WAKE YOURSELF UP WITH MORE THAN JUST A COFFEE AT THE BEAR-FIT WEEKLY BOOTCAMP

Pick up a grin-inducing gluten-free bake while you're waiting, or pop next door for a Mexican-inspired Bearrito from the double decker bus cantina.

ESTABLISHED
2013

KEY ROASTER
Wogan Coffee

BREWING METHOD
Espresso, filter

MACHINE
Astoria Plus
4 You

GRINDER
Fiorenzato F38

OPENING HOURS
Mon-Fri
7am-6pm
Sat 10am-6pm

---

www.bearpitbristol.co.uk   T: 07786 927555

f Bearpit Social   🐦 @bearpitsocial   📷 @bearpitsocial

№27. ROLLING ITALY

Woodland Road, Clifton, Bristol, BS8 1US

№27. ROLLING ITALY

Woodland Road, Clifton, Bristol, BS8 1US

The imminent arrival of one's first child is a time for hunkering down, reducing stress and preparing for the colossal change on the horizon, right? Not for James and Chloe Staunton, who chose that moment to launch their speciality coffee business on wheels.

Their accomplice is a rather handsome Italian – an authentic Piaggio Ape transformed into a mini osteria. And with a second van joining the family, there will soon be even more opportunities to visit the mobile espresso bars at a range of events across Bristol.

INSIDER'S TIP
PAIR YOUR COFFEE WITH ONE OF JAMES' ORANGE AND ALMOND RICCIARELLI BISCUITS

Rolling Italy's small but perfectly formed shop front is echoed in James and Chloe's focus on doing just a few things well, having limited themselves to a concise espresso-based menu to fit the space.

Extract provides the beans of choice, with guest roasters popping up from time to time. James, who worked as a chef for years says, *'I've brought my passion for sourcing the best produce and creating something amazing to the venture. There's nothing quite like seeing the smile on a customer's face when we present them with a coffee that not only looks spectacular, but tastes great too.'*

ESTABLISHED
2014

KEY ROASTER
Extract Coffee Roasters

BREWING METHOD
Espresso, AeroPress, cold brew

MACHINE
Rancilio, Fracino dual fuel

GRINDER
Mahlkonig K30, Sanremo SR50, Mazzer Mini

OPENING HOURS
Mon-Fri
8am-2pm (Woodland Road)
Sun 10am-2.30pm (Tobacco Factory)

Gluten FREE

ALTERNATIVE MILK

CYCLE FRIENDLY

DISABLED ACCESS

T: 07824 441785

f Rolling Italy   🐦 @rollingitaly   📷 @rolling_italy

№28. BOSTON TEA PARTY – PARK STREET

75 Park Street, Bristol, BS1 5PF

Flying the flag as Boston's inaugural cafe – and doing the speciality thing way before it went mainstream – the Park Street pad has firmly established itself as a Bristol coffee institution since opening two decades ago.

The scrumptious spot churns out first-class brunches and cracking brews at a rate of knots. And it's not only customers that it serves; it's doing its bit to help the planet and local community too.

INSIDER'S TIP STOP BY FOR AN EARLY BITE – IT WAS VOTED IN THE TOP 25 FOR BRUNCH BY THE TIMES

The periodically-packed cafe received three stars from the Sustainable Restaurant Association, as well as the Biggest Commitment to Sustainability award from Bristol Good Food, which is high praise among the bevy of ethical employers in the eco-focused city.

Extract's South American beans resonate with notes of chocolate, caramel and hazelnut for medium, dark and decaf roasts while regularly changing filter coffees provide seasonal alternatives for those looking to expand their brew horizons.

ESTABLISHED
1995

KEY ROASTER
Extract Coffee Roasters

BREWING METHOD
Espresso, filter

MACHINE
La Marzocco PB

GRINDER
Mythos One

OPENING HOURS
Mon-Sat
7am-8pm
Sun
8am-7pm

---

www.bostonteaparty.co.uk   T: 01179 298601

f Boston Tea Party Cafés   🐦 @btpcafes   📷 @btpcafes

MAP№ 29. SMALL STREET ESPRESSO

23 Small Street, Bristol, BS1 1DW

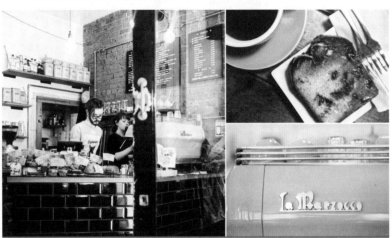

Celebrating its fifth birthday in December 2017, Small Street Espresso was one of the trailblazing coffee shops which first planted the speciality seed in Bristol.

Clifton Coffee, fellow pioneer in the caffeine-curious city, has supplied the piccolo-sized cafe with beautifully roasted beans from day one. Its seasonal EQ blend – currently a cracking combination of pink grapefruit, cherry and butterscotch notes – is used to fashion vibrant espressos from the sky blue La Marzocco machine.

INSIDER'S TIP GET HERE EARLY FOR YOUR PICK OF THE HART'S BAKERY PASTRIES

Notable names from the UK roasting repertoire offer alternatives via espresso, AeroPress and cold brew – look out for single origins from the likes of Yallah, Nude, Round Hill, Studio and Extract.

The team's unpretentious and friendly service has earned Small Street a cohort of coffee-chugging regulars. There are no tables or chairs, just a few communal benches and casual stools, so squeeze up for some home brewing pointers and cake recommendations from the locals.

ESTABLISHED
2012

KEY ROASTER
Clifton Coffee Roasters

BREWING METHOD
Espresso, AeroPress, cold brew

MACHINE
La Marzocco FB80

GRINDER
Mythos x 2, Mahlkonig Tanzania

OPENING HOURS
Mon-Fri
7.30am-4.30pm
Sat-Sun
9.30am-4.30pm

www.smallstreetespresso.co.uk

f Small St. Espresso 🐦 @smallstespresso 📷 @smallstespresso

One Simple Mission
MAKE COFFEE

BETTER

 for farmers

 for baristas

 for roasters

 for drinkers

E EXTRACT COFFEE ROASTERS

EXTRACTCOFFEE.CO.UK

Roasted in Brizzle since 2007

MAP№ 30. PLAYGROUND COFFEE & BAR

45 St Nicholas Street, Bristol, BS1 1TP

Extending playtime after hours, the big kids behind Bristol's convivial coffee bar have added a curious collection of prohibition-inspired cocktails to its offering this year.

This tipsy addition doesn't spell a diversion from speciality though, as owners Fabian and Lilly have teamed up with local distillery Psychopomp to craft the first gin to use coffee as a botanical. Try it straight up with tonic or incorporated in one of the coffee-infused concoctions during the new late opening hours.

INSIDER'S TIP WE'RE CALLING IT: THE MR BLACK NEGRONI IS THE NEXT ESPRESSO MARTINI

Playground's daytime guise, however, is still all about its stonking selection of single origins from across the UK and Europe. Roasters come and go as quickly as a round of KerPlunk (one of the 150 board games to challenge your coffee-chugging chums to), though beans from Bath's Colonna Coffee are a frequent feature.

Lilly's homemade sweet thrills such as intensely gooey brownies continue to fuel tense chess matches and entertain the lunch-break crowd making the most of the in-house swing set.

ESTABLISHED
2014

KEY ROASTER
Colonna Coffee

BREWING METHOD
Espresso, Kalita Wave, V60, syphon, AeroPress, Chemex

MACHINE
La Marzocco Linea

GRINDER
Mahlkonig K30 twin

OPENING HOURS
Mon-Wed
8.30am-5pm
Thu-Fri
8.30am-11pm
Sat 10.30am-11pm
Sun 11.30am-4.30pm

 Gluten FREE

 BEANS AVAILABLE INSTORE

 ALTERNATIVE MILK

 WIFI

 CYCLE FRIENDLY

 OUTDOOR SEATING

 DISABLED ACCESS

 BRING YOUR OWN Cup

COFFEE COURSES

---

www.playgroundcoffee.co.uk

f Playground Coffee House 🐦 @playgroundcofco

№31. SPICER+COLE

1 Queen Square Avenue, Bristol, BS1 4JA

It's no mean feat stocking a counter of toothsome bakes, crafting a homemade menu and brewing first-class coffee all under one roof, but after almost five years in the game it comes naturally to Spicer+Cole owners, Carla and Chris Swift.

The original cafe – you'll find another in Clifton and one on Gloucester Road – inhabits leafy Queen Square, a sunny spot in the city centre that's a mere stone skim from the harbour.

It's here that two-wheeled commuters make a pit-stop for their espresso hit and freelancers fuel their daily grind with the latest single origin.

INSIDER'S TIP A SLICE OF THE ZESTY LIME AND COURGETTE CAKE COUNTS AS ONE OF YOUR FIVE-A-DAY, RIGHT?

Come lunchtime, the stripped-back space is stacked with foodies getting their fill of locally sourced salads and seasonal savouries, while the cake bounty is in demand by families and dog walkers all day.

For specialist sipping, Extract does the honours as the house coffee while South West roasters Crankhouse and Little and Long join big names such as Workshop and The Barn as guests. Loose-leaf enthusiasts enjoy an equally artisan offering from Cardiff's Waterloo Tea, along with cold-pressed juices and smoothies.

ESTABLISHED
2012

KEY ROASTER
Extract Coffee
Roasters

BREWING METHOD
Espresso,
cold brew

MACHINE
Sanremo TCS

GRINDER
Mythos

OPENING HOURS
Mon-Fri
7.30am-4pm
Sat-Sun
9am-4pm

---

www.spicerandcole.co.uk   T: 01179 220513

f Spicer and Cole   🐦 @spicerandcole   📷 @spicerandcole

32. SOCIETY CAFE – HARBOURSIDE

Farrs Lane, Narrow Quay, Bristol, BS1 4BD

After garnering a fanbase of coffee swiggin' enthusiasts in Bath, Society Cafe added a fourth venue to its growing collection in 2017 – this time at a former rope factory on Bristol's Harbourside.

Like its sister venues, the cafe is packed to the rafters with custom-made cool, from tables and cute cubic stools to light fittings and a bespoke bar.

With over 70 seats, there's plenty of space for Bristol's bean geeks to hunker down with a brew and admire the carpenters' handiwork and the local photography adorning the walls.

INSIDER'S TIP CHECK OUT THE WALL MURALS WHICH WERE PAINTED BY THE SOCIETY CLAN

Coffee – espresso based, filter, AeroPress and cold brew – is supplied by house favourite Origin, and the baristas work closely with the Cornish roaster, even accompanying them on a Nicaraguan trip to see the coffee at source.

A gaggle of guests including Round Hill, The Barn and Colonna provide additional interest, as do on-site courses and cupping evenings.

ESTABLISHED
2017

KEY ROASTER
Origin Coffee Roasters

BREWING METHOD
Espresso, V60, AeroPress, cold brew

MACHINE
La Marzocco Linea PB

GRINDER
Mythos One

OPENING HOURS
Mon-Sat
7.30am-6.30pm
Sun
10am-6pm

www.society-cafe.com   T: 01179 304660

f Society Cafe   🐦 @societycafe   📷 @societycafe

№33. LITTLE VICTORIES

7 Gaol Ferry Steps, Wapping Wharf, Bristol, BS1 6WE

Starting the day with an exceptional cup of coffee is one of life's little victories: a triumph the team at this waterside coffee shop fulfil every morning.

With a sweet corner spot at Wapping Wharf – all high ceilings, geometric fittings and bleached wood – Little Vics fuels city slickers, savvy shoppers and creative folk with top-notch espresso and filters.

Local roaster Clifton supplies the punchy seasonal EQ blend at this sister cafe to Small Street Espresso, while monthly guests fill the single origin and filter spots at the brew bar. There's also slow-drip house cold brew and alfresco seating for summer sipping.

INSIDER'S TIP SWING BY AFTER HOURS FOR WHAT COULD BE THE BEST ESPRESSO MARTINI IN BRISTOL

Speciality proceedings continue into the evening with coffee cocktails and a selection of craft beers and natural wines. A pit-stop for a cold brew negroni and local charcuterie board before heading to dinner at one of the Wharf's indies is a real winner.

ESTABLISHED
2016

KEY ROASTER
Clifton Coffee Roasters

BREWING METHOD
Espresso, Chemex, cold brew

MACHINE
Victoria Arduino Black Eagle

GRINDER
Mythos One x 3, Mahlkonig EK 43

OPENING HOURS
Mon 7.30am-4.30pm
Tue-Wed 7.30am-7pm
Thu-Fri 7.30am-10pm
Sat 9.30am-10.30pm
Sun 9.30am-4.30pm

---

www.littlevics.co.uk
f Little Victories 🐦 @littlevicsbris 📷 @littlevicsbris

34. MOKOKO COFFEE – WAPPING WHARF

2 Gaol Ferry Steps, Wapping Wharf, Bristol, BS1 6WE

Since opening in 2016, Mokoko has established itself as a go-to for a great pour at the heart of Bristol's hip Wapping Wharf.

The outside seating area, with its bright blue chairs, adds a vibrant splash of colour along the tree-lined walkway, while inside it's bright and airy with big windows and an industrial, Scandi feel. Blue tiled walls and daffodil yellow espresso machines bring warmth to simple wood and metal furnishings.

INSIDER'S TIP: THE CRUFFIN WITH PASSION FRUIT CURD AND LEMON BALM IS A GAME CHANGER

Via its longer established sister shops in Bath (where it was founded), Mokoko carries a reputation for a finely perfected coffee experience.

Bristolians also get to enjoy its fabulous in-shop bakery which is responsible for the mountain of cakes and pastries piled on the counter.

Grab a table near the bakers and watch them work on the next batch of cakes and croissants, or pull up a stool in front of the floor-to-ceiling windows and observe the world drift by as you linger over a pourover.

ESTABLISHED
2016

KEY ROASTER
Mokoko, Extract Coffee Roasters, James Gourmet Coffee

BREWING METHOD
Espresso, pourover

MACHINE
Conti Monte Carlo x 2

GRINDER
Mahlkonig K30, Compak E10, Compak E8, Compak R120

OPENING HOURS
Mon-Fri
7.30am-5.30pm
Sat 8am-6.30pm

www.mokokocoffee.com T: 0117 9290177
f Mokoko Coffee 🐦 @mokokocoffee 📷 @mokokocoffee

MAP № 35. TINCAN COFFEE CO.

234 North Street, Southville, Bristol, BS3 1JD

Tincan's roots go back to 2011, when it began serving speciality brews to caffeine-craving, wellie-clad festival goers from its fleet of roving coffee trucks.

The mobile espresso bars continue to thrive but the Tincan brand is also firmly cemented as a less moveable feast in Southville, where it has brewed up a loyal following for its revolving line-up of guest espressos and single origin filters.

INSIDER'S TIP CHECK OUT THE HEADLAMPS AND SEATS WHICH TIP THEIR HAT TO TINCAN'S TRUCKS

Appetites are sated through a sterling selection of cakes, cold-pressed juices and sourdough toasties, along with creative kitchen specials crafted from locally sourced ingredients. Check out the brunch bill for reconditioned classics such as the Mexican breakfast of champions, huevos rancheros: baked eggs, black turtle beans and chipotle and coriander pesto crowning chewy sourdough.

Drop by on a Friday for sweet indulgence: eton mess, chocolate fudge brownies and sour cherry bakewell doughnuts all deserve a moment of recognition.

ESTABLISHED
2016

KEY ROASTER
Clifton Coffee
Roasters

BREWING METHOD
Espresso,
batch filter

MACHINE
La Marzocco
Linea PB

GRINDER
Mythos One

OPENING HOURS
Mon-Sat
8am-6pm
Sun 9am-5pm

Gluten FREE

BEANS AVAILABLE INSTORE

ALTERNATIVE MILK

WIFI

CYCLE FRIENDLY

OUTDOOR SEATING

FAMILY FRIENDLY

DISABLED ACCESS

---

www.tincancoffee.co.uk   T: 01179 633979

f Tincan Coffee Co   🐦 @tincancoffeeco   📷 @tincancoffeeco

ℵ36. TINCAN COFFEE CO. TRUCKS

Music festivals and high profile sporting events around the UK

A pioneer in the resurgence of vintage catering vehicles, Tincan's herd of 60s and 70s restored coffee trucks burst with top-end espresso kit and bags of personality.

Back in 2011 the team met Claude, a dishevelled ex-delivery truck, which after thorough restoration was sent out as the very first Tincan coffee van.

INSIDER'S TIP BRISTOLIANS CAN GET THEIR FIX AT THE GANG'S SOUTHVILLE COFFEE SHOP

A bevy of love affairs later (Wilfred, Dennis, Woody, Napolean, Alfie ...) and the show is very successfully on the road. The Tincan posse have brewed up at a FOMO inducing line-up of festivals and events across the country including Secret Garden Party, Wilderness and Latitude.

Carrying their cargo of carefully crafted Clifton coffee, the Tincan trucks are a familiar sight during weekend merrymaking. With iced blends, an extensive list of milk alternatives, award winning cakes and kick ass tunes – as well as expertly pulled espresso – festival goers have never had it so good.

ESTABLISHED
2011

KEY ROASTER
Clifton Coffee Roasters

BREWING METHOD
Espresso

MACHINE
La Spaziale S5

GRINDER
Mazzer

OPENING HOURS
As per event

Gluten FREE

ALTERNATIVE MILK

OUTDOOR seating

FAMILY friendly

BRING YOUR OWN Cup

---

www.tincancoffee.co.uk/events   T: 07725 880581

f Tincan Coffee Co   🐦 @tincancoffeeco   📷 @tincancoffeeco

ROASTERS BRISTOL

ROASTED RITUALS COFFEE #40

MAP 37. COLONNA COFFEE

Unit 5, Apollo Park, Armstrong Way, Yate, Bristol, BS37 5AH

It was only natural that the team of leading speciality purveyors at Bath's Colonna & Small's would expand into the world of roasting.

Setting up Colonna Coffee on the outskirts of the city in 2015, the roastery specialises in showcasing seasonal, single origin and small lot beans in a stripped-back selection of coffees which changes every four to six weeks.

ESTABLISHED
2015

ROASTER
MAKE & SIZE
Diedrich
12kg,
CR35 35kg

BEANS AVAILABLE

ONLINE

'WE WANTED TO FOCUS ON EXCITING SMALL LOTS, SEEKING TO EXPLORE CHARACTER AND VARIETY WITH AN ASSORTMENT OF CAREFULLY SOURCED SPECTACULAR COFFEES'

With no blends and only top grade coffees in the collection, Colonna beans are frequently found on guest spots at specialist cafes across the UK and Europe, often served using unique and exploratory brewing methods. Turning heads in the industry, Colonna continues to challenge the single serve capsule system's corporate reputation with a game-changing range of speciality coffee pods. Not ones to sit still, the team have also dabbled in science this year, co-authoring academic papers on topics such as freezing beans and the effect of water on flavour.

www.colonnacoffee.com

f Colonna 🐦 @colonnacoffee 📷 @colonnacoffee

MAP 38. CLIFTON COFFEE ROASTERS

Unit C2, Island Trade Park, Bristow Broadway, Avonmouth, Bristol, BS11 9FB

'**O**ur aim is to provide solutions,' explains Josh Clarke, whose coffee creds have recently landed him a new role at the Bristol roastery: head of coffee. With that title, he's clearly Clifton's guy to turn to for caffeinated consultation.

Making a name for itself in the speciality trade over the past 15 years, Clifton remains a top choice for cafes, bars, restaurants and hotels across the region and in the further reaches of the UK.

Working directly with producers in El Salvador as well as with speciality importers, the team continue to gather unique, distinctive and seasonal beans from Africa and South America. In fact, the bright and juicy EQ Seasonal Espresso is now in its 12th incarnation: *It's taken from the idea of an audio equaliser on an old fashioned amplifier, as the key to this blend is balance,*' says Josh.

'THE TEAM CONTINUE TO GATHER UNIQUE, DISTINCTIVE AND SEASONAL BEANS FROM AFRICA AND AMERICA'

Providing bags of support to its customers remains a key part of the package, from machine engineering through to training – Coffee Masters London and New York finalist Jimmy Dimitrov brews up batches of brilliant baristas at Clifton's SCA training program.

ESTABLISHED
2001

ROASTER
MAKE & SIZE
Diedrich IR 12kg,
Diedrich CR 25kg,
Diedrich CR 35kg

OPEN
BY APPOINTMENT

OPEN
TO THE PUBLIC

COFFEE
COURSES

COURSES

BEANS
AVAILABLE

ONLINE

www.cliftoncoffee.co.uk   T: 01179 820252

f Clifton Coffee Roasters   🐦 @cliftoncoffee   📷 @cliftoncoffee

39. EXTRACT COFFEE ROASTERS

Unit 1, Gatton Road, Bristol, BS2 9SH

It's been another action packed year for the team of roasters, trainers and baristas at Extract's Bristol HQ. 2017 saw numerous trips to origin and Dave returned to the mountains of Peru as part of Extract's ongoing partnership with an organic cooperative of smallholders, Sol & Café.

'Introducing the cooperative's coffee to our hero range and speciality filter sachets is an exciting step,' explains director Marc. 'Our customers get 100 per cent traceability from crop to cup, and we're driving real change in the lives of the coffee farmers and their communities.'

Then there's the awesome training team schooling budding baristas to SCA standards. 'We're keen to make training as accessible as possible,' says head trainer Dan Lacey, 'so that customers can now choose from free training at the roastery or at their own location.'

And who could forget South West account manager – and superstar barista – Callum Parsons who scooped fourth prize at the 2017 UK Barista Champs?

Meanwhile the team continue to crank out their popular seasonal single origin espressos alongside a catalogue of crowd-pleasing hero coffees and globe-trotting filters.

ESTABLISHED
2007

ROASTER
MAKE & SIZE
Probat 120kg,
Probat 60kg,
Petrocini 30kg,
Ozturk 4kg

OPEN
BY APPOINTMENT

COFFEE COURSES

COURSES

BEANS AVAILABLE
ONSITE

ONLINE

www.extractcoffee.co.uk   T: 01179 554976

Extract Coffee Roasters   @extractcoffee   @extractcoffee

40. ROASTED RITUALS COFFEE

Unit 18, Kenn Court, Roman Farm Road, Bristol, BS4 1UL

'*Every detail counts when you're running a cafe*,' says Patrick Grant-Sturgis of Bristol's Roasted Rituals Coffee. '*The whole package needs to be complete: every ingredient, every placement and every sensory experience.*'

Which is where the Roasted Rituals team come in. The talented bunch, who have been roasting speciality coffee in Bristol since 2012, offer a range of rotating single origin coffees as well as their increasingly popular Highground blend.

THEY ALSO OFFER BARISTA TRAINING, ROASTERY TOURS, CUPPING SESSIONS AND CUSTOMER SERVICE

'*With years of experience, commitment to quality and great attention to detail, we offer coffees that strike the senses so that imbibing them is an experience,*' continues Patrick. '*With a focus on cleanness and balance, our Highground blend punches through milk as well as shining on its own.*'

Ethics are also high on the agenda and many of the coffees are organic and Rainforest Alliance certified.

'*We make sure that the producer benefits financially, and we share knowledge with them in order to create a better working environment and boost quality,*' says Patrick.

ESTABLISHED
2012

ROASTER
MAKE & SIZE
Probat 12kg

OPEN
BY APPOINTMENT

OPEN
TO THE PUBLIC

COFFEE
COURSES

CUPPING
EVENTS

BEANS
AVAILABLE

ONSITE

ONLINE

www.roastedritualscoffee.com   T: 01172 440098

f Roasted Rituals Coffee   🐦 @roastedrituals   📷 @roastedritualscoffee

BATH & SOMERSET

THE BATH
COFFEE
COMPANY
#47

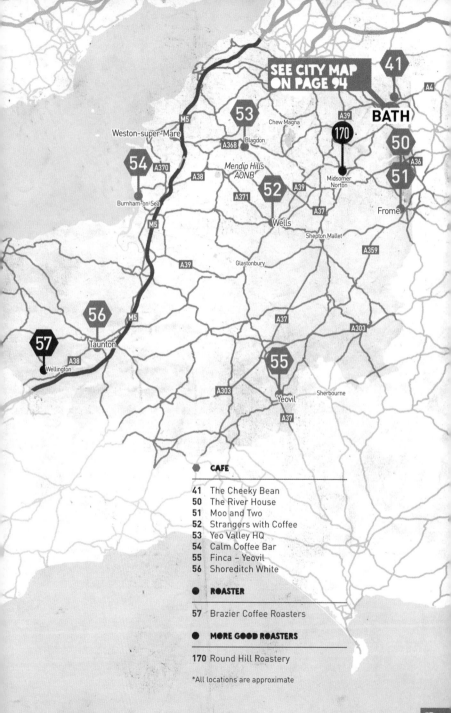

SEE CITY MAP
ON PAGE 94

41

A4

53

Chew Magna

BATH

170

A39

50

Weston-super-Mare

A368

Blagdon

54

A370

Mendip Hills
AONB

A38

A371

52

A39

Midsomer
Norton

A36

51

Burnham-on-Sea

A37

Frome

M5

Wells

A359

Shepton Mallet

A39

Glastonbury

56

M5

A37

A303

Taunton

57

A38

Wellington

A303

55

Yeovil

Sherbourne

A37

● **CAFE**

41   The Cheeky Bean
50   The River House
51   Moo and Two
52   Strangers with Coffee
53   Yeo Valley HQ
54   Calm Coffee Bar
55   Finca – Yeovil
56   Shoreditch White

● **ROASTER**

57   Brazier Coffee Roasters

● **MORE GOOD ROASTERS**

170 Round Hill Roastery

*All locations are approximate

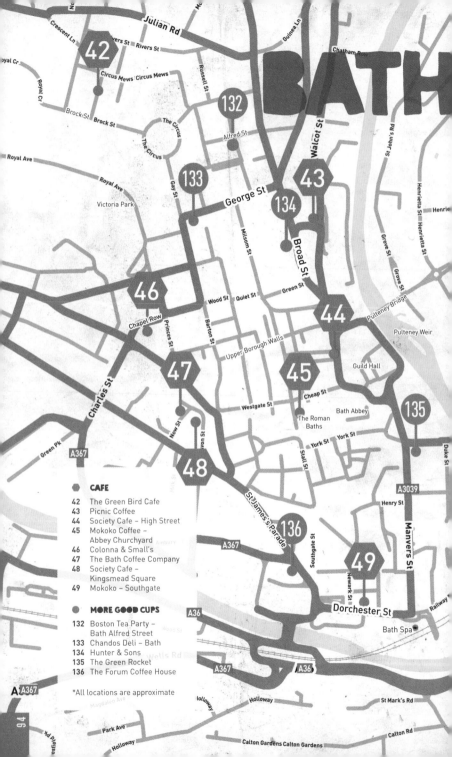

CAFE

42 The Green Bird Cafe
43 Picnic Coffee
44 Society Cafe – High Street
45 Mokoko Coffee –
    Abbey Churchyard
46 Colonna & Small's
47 The Bath Coffee Company
48 Society Cafe –
    Kingsmead Square
49 Mokoko – Southgate

MORE GOOD CUPS

132 Boston Tea Party –
     Bath Alfred Street
133 Chandos Deli – Bath
134 Hunter & Sons
135 The Green Rocket
136 The Forum Coffee House

*All locations are approximate

MAP № 41. THE CHEEKY BEAN

2 Balustrade, London Road, Bath, BA1 6QA

With a paint palette to wake even the weariest of early morning caffeine seekers, The Cheeky Bean (all Indian-inspired colours, cool music, resident disco ball and positive vibes) is a welcome addition to Bath's specialist scene.

Step through the turquoise arch for a brew 'n' bake and it won't be long before you're on first name terms with this friendly bunch – including Mabel the resident pooch.

INSIDER'S TIP DODGING DAIRY? TRY THE OATLY BARISTA EDITION AS A NON-SWEET ALTERNATIVE

On the specialist side, Wiltshire-based Dusty Ape fills the hopper with richly roasted, small batch beans: pick up an espresso or filter brew to savour its signature toffee tones. And while you're supping, browse the menu for scrumptious salad boxes, made-to-order breakfasts, chunky sarnies and homemade cakes.

Inspired by their field-frequenting festival days, the gang also ensure caffeine-craving gadabouts get their fix via The Cheeky Bean tuk-tuk-turned-espresso-bar which delivers fresh brews to less-than-fresh festival goers.

ESTABLISHED
2016

KEY ROASTER
Dusty Ape

BREWING METHOD
Espresso, filter

MACHINE
La Spaziale S2

GRINDER
Macap MXDL

OPENING HOURS
Mon-Fri
7.30am-3pm
Sat
9.30am-2.30pm
Sun
9.30am-2.30pm

 Gluten FREE

 ALTERNATIVE MILK

 WIFI

 CYCLE FRIENDLY

 OUTDOOR Seating

 DISABLED ACCESS

---

www.thecheekybean.co.uk   T: 01225 313003

 The Cheeky Bean   🐦 @cheekybeanbath   📷 @thecheekybeanbath

MAP № 42. THE GREEN BIRD CAFE

11 Margaret's Buildings, Bath, BA1 2LP

We really shouldn't be publicising Bath's Green Bird Cafe, because in a city that's thronging with tourists most of the year, this is a local coffee lover's little secret, tucked away between the Royal Crescent and the Circus.

Okay, it won *Bath Life*'s Best Cafe in 2016, but it's still very much a neighbourhood fave, partly due to its secluded suntrap courtyard which provides an oasis of coffee calm amid the touristy madness.

INSIDER'S TIP THESE GUYS RECENTLY SCOOPED BEST BREKKIE IN THE CITY AT THE BATH GOOD FOOD AWARDS

We'd recommend starting your morning in simple pared-back style at The Green Bird with a Wogan espresso based brew and a couple of slices of chewy, buttered sourdough toast from the city's most famous baker, Richard Bertinet. Or swing by later for a sarnie lunch of salt beef, emmental and dill pickle with salad, or the popular mature cheddar toastie with hand-carved ham and mustard.

The recent funky interior refurb has included some new coffee gear for the gang to play with, and the La Marzocco PB espresso machine and Mahlkonig K30 grinder are taking this little bird to new heights.

ESTABLISHED
2015

KEY ROASTER
Wogan Coffee

BREWING METHOD
Espresso

MACHINE
La Marzocco Linea PB

GRINDER
Mahlkonig K30

OPENING HOURS
Mon-Sat
8am-5pm
Sun
10am-4pm

www.greenbirdcafe.co.uk T: 01225 487846
f The Green Bird Cafe 🐦 @greenbirdcafe 📷 @thegreenbirdcafe

MAP № 43. PICNIC COFFEE

9 Saracen Street, Bath, BA1 5BR

If you're curious about drinking coffee that tastes exactly how the grower and roaster intended, then Picnic Coffee in Bath should be on your hit list.

The team taste test before picking the best brew method for the top-notch single origin coffees which arrive in small batches from roaster Union. And as a result, owners Tim and Kate and baristas Jenn, Rachael and Tessa love to guide customers through tasting notes and serve-style combos.

Whether you swing by for a fast fix on the way to work or have time to fritter, the coffee landscape is also kept interesting via guest roasts from local roasteries such as Round Hill.

INSIDER'S TIP CANINE-LOVING COFFEE ADDICTS TAKE NOTE – DOGS ARE WELCOME HERE

A welcoming mix of travel books, cosy armchairs, outdoor seating and homemade cakes and savouries are encouragement to stick around at this sociable hub.

And, come evening, the regular live music night, Picnic Unplugged, is an opportunity to quaff craft beers, wines or espressos as you get your groove on to local bands.

ESTABLISHED
2013

KEY ROASTER
Union Hand-Roasted Coffee

BREWING METHOD
Espresso, AeroPress, filter, V60, pourover

MACHINE
Victoria Arduino Black Eagle

GRINDER
Mahlkonig K30, Mahlkonig Vario x 2, Mazzer Jolly

OPENING HOURS
Mon-Fri
7.30am-6pm
Sat 8.30am-6pm
Sun 9am-6pm

 Gluten FREE

 BEANS AVAILABLE INSTORE

 ALTERNATIVE MILK

 WIFI

 CYCLE FRIENDLY

 OUTDOOR SEATING

 FAMILY FRIENDLY

 DISABLED ACCESS

---

www.picniccoffee.co.uk   T: 01225 330128

f Picnic Coffee   🐦 @picnic_bath   📷 @picnic_bath

№ 44. SOCIETY CAFE – HIGH STREET

19 High Street, Bath, BA1 5AJ

little but lovely, Kingsmead's smaller Bath sibling is a real charmer. Owners Adrian and Jane Campbell-Howard have boldly taken on the high street's big brand coffee shops, keen to prove that you don't need to go off the beaten track to enjoy a quality cup.

With a clean-cut design and a small clutch of seats up and downstairs, you need to get in early to nab somewhere to savour your pastry and piccolo, so grab-and-gos are popular here.

INSIDER'S TIP THE TEAM'S PRIDE AND JOY IS A KOREAN RIDGE BREWER WHICH PRODUCES BATCHES OF COLD BREW

Armed with two new Mythos One grinders and recent batch and cold brew additions on the menu, the baristas are building a firm fanbase at Society's second outpost in the city.

Ongoing collaborations with Cornish roaster Origin resulted in an eye-opening trip to Nicaragua last March. After meeting the awe-inspiring Mierisch family farmers, the team returned laden with a stonking new house bean, Las Colinas. Sample the South American beauty with a local sarnie or a slab of cake.

ESTABLISHED
2014

KEY ROASTER
Origin Coffee
Roasters

BREWING METHOD
Espresso,
AeroPress, Clever
Dripper, batch
brew, cold brew

MACHINE
La Marzocco Linea PB

GRINDER
Mahlkonig K30
Twin Vario,
Mahlkonig EK 43,
Nuova Simonelli
Mythos x 2

OPENING HOURS
Mon-Sat
7.30am-6.30pm
Sun 9am-6pm

www.society-cafe.com   T: 01225 428008

f Society Cafe   🐦 @societycafe   📷 @societycafe

MAP 45. MOKOKO COFFEE – ABBEY CHURCHYARD

6 Abbey Churchyard, Bath, BA1 1LY

The former Jacob's Coffee House has been refurbished and also rebranded this year, clarifying its connection to its sister shops in Southgate and Bristol's Wapping Wharf.

This is where the Mokoko story began, and it continues its mission to serve expertly made, great coffee in a friendly and approachable way.

INSIDER'S TIP TAKE YOUR COFFEE ALFRESCO, WATCHING BATH'S STREET PERFORMERS FROM THE COURTYARD

A variety of roasters and coffees keeps things fresh and interesting and, along with the other changes (including the introduction of reverse osmosis), a new menu has arrived packed with quiches, imaginative salads and inspired cakes and pastries, all of which are made on site or at the Bristol store's in-house bakery.

Set in the city's chain-filled shopping centre, it's a treat to discover a genuine speciality coffee experience. Just a step away from the Abbey, the place is also steeped in Georgian history, so with a little imagination you get a flavour of the city's coffee houses of centuries past, while indulging in a contemporary, ever changing range of espresso and filter options.

ESTABLISHED
2011

KEY ROASTER
Mokoko, James Gourmet Coffee, Clifton Coffee Roasters

BREWING METHOD
Espresso, Marco Jet

MACHINE
Conti Monte Carlo

GRINDER
Compak E10 Master Conic x 2, Compak E6

OPENING HOURS
Mon-Sat
8am-6pm
Sun 9am-6pm

 Gluten FREE

 BEANS AVAILABLE INSTORE

 ALTERNATIVE MILK

 WIFI

 CYCLE FRIENDLY

 OUTDOOR seating

 FAMILY FRIENDLY

www.mokokocoffee.com   T: 01225 758132

f Mokoko Coffee   🐦 @mokokocoffee   📷 @mokokocoffee

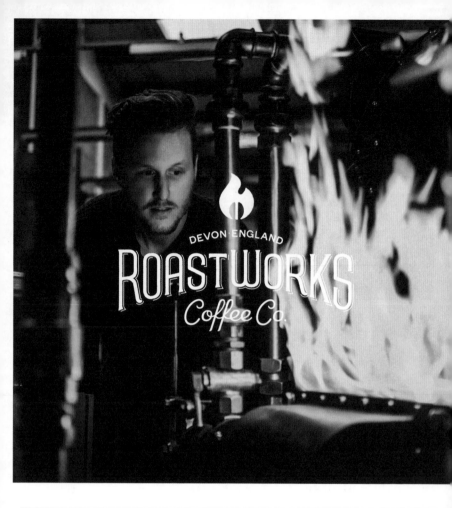

SPECIALITY COFFEE ROASTED IN DEVON

WE'RE A SMALL, INDEPENDENT COFFEE ROASTER DEDICATED TO REDEFINING CONSUMER COFFEE BY MAKING SPECIALITY COFFEE ACCESSIBLE TO EVERYONE. WE SOURCE EXCEPTIONAL SEASONAL BEANS FROM AROUND THE WORLD WHICH WE ROAST IN A WAY TO HIGHLIGHT THEIR INTRINSIC QUALITIES USING OUR VINTAGE GERMAN DRUM ROASTER.

INSTAGRAM.COM/ROASTWORKS_COFFEE_CO
@ROASTWORKSDEVON
FB.COM/ROASTWORKSCOFFEECO
ROASTWORKS.CO.UK

MAP 46. COLONNA & SMALL'S

6 Chapel Row, Bath, BA1 1HN

This cathedral to coffee in historic Bath has become synonymous with speciality in the South West. Colonna's success and status within the industry comes as no surprise as co-owner – and three time UK barista champ – Maxwell Colonna-Dashwood has been a pioneer in the speciality movement for almost a decade.

In the past few years, the pared-back coffee shop has progressed from simply crafting first-class coffee to brewing its own range of seasonally-led single origin espressos and fine filters, which are roasted just outside the city.

'Our passion for customer service and the pursuit of flavour, character and the experience that coffee can generate is at the core of what we do,' explains Maxwell.

INSIDER'S TIP SWOT UP ON YOUR SPECIALITY SPIEL WITH MAXWELL'S NEW BOOK, THE COFFEE DICTIONARY

A sleek bar focuses visitors' attention on the preparation of the beans and allows baristas to chat about the brewing methods and characteristics of each cup. And in addition to speciality disciples on a pilgrimage to Colonna, you'll also find coffee novices popping in to experience the pour.

ESTABLISHED
2009

KEY ROASTER
Colonna Coffee

BREWING METHOD
Espresso, lungo, AeroPress, syphon

MACHINE
Modbar

GRINDER
Mahlkonig EK 43

OPENING HOURS
Mon-Fri
8am-5.30pm
Sat
8.30am-5.30pm
Sun
10am-4pm

 Gluten FREE
 BEANS AVAILABLE INSTORE
 ALTERNATIVE MILK
 WIFI
 OUTDOOR seating
 BRING YOUR OWN Cup

www.colonnaandsmalls.co.uk   T: 07766 808067

f Colonna   🐦 @colonna_smalls   📷 @colonnacoffee

MAP № 47. THE BATH COFFEE COMPANY

14 Kingsmead Square, Bath, BA1 2AD

'It's all about the coffee,' may be the motto at The Bath Coffee Company, but clearly this cosy indie overlooking Kingsmead Square is also all about well prepared drinks, daily-changing cakes and pastries, and in-depth coffee chat.

Multi-skilled owner Adrian spends his time hot footing it from the cafe (where he pulls the shots) to Square Root roastery in Wiltshire, where he calls the shots as master roaster.

INSIDER'S TIP
CATCH OWNER AND ROASTER ADRIAN ON SITE FOR A CHAT – HE LOVES TO TALK COFFEE

Tracking coffee from farm to cup, he ensures that the menu hosts a range of espresso and filters to please both the caffeine curious and discerning Bath regulars.

Beans are only ever ground to order, and a good place to begin is with the house favourite: a piccolo latte made with a smooth Brazilian-Indian-Sumatran blend called The Solution.

For a cosy caffeinated experience, seek out some sofa time in the downstairs space where you can get your nose stuck into a novel or have a bash at a board game as you slurp.

ESTABLISHED
2014

KEY ROASTER
Square Root Coffee

BREWING METHOD
Espresso, V60, AeroPress

MACHINE
La Pavoni

GRINDER
La Pavoni, Graef, Cunhill

OPENING HOURS
Mon-Sun
8am-6pm

www.bathcoffeecompany.co.uk   T: 07940 120835
f The Bath Coffee Company   🐦 @thebathcoffeeco   📷 @bathcoffeecompany

MAP 48. SOCIETY CAFE – KINGSMEAD SQUARE

5 Kingsmead Square, Bath, BA1 2AB

The original cafe in Society's growing caffeine fraternity, the Kingsmead Square hangout is a firm favourite among Bath's band of espresso houses and brew bars.

In keeping with the city's increasing interest in speciality, batch brew has made it onto the Society menu this year, adding a speedy filter fix to the brew bar inventory.

The current beans of choice – Las Colinas from the Mierisch family farm – were sourced by the team during a recent trip to Nicaragua with house roaster, Origin.

INSIDER'S TIP SOCIETY ALSO STOCKS A STERLING COLLECTION OF TEAS

And quite an experience it was too: *'It was amazing to see how well the farmers looked after their team. When you drink a cup of coffee you don't wonder "where do the farmers' kids go to school?" or "what does their work look like?". We love the fact that we're supporting families through our work with Origin,'* explain Adrian and Jane, the friendly faces behind Society.

The clan may be assisting international communities through coffee, but they also support businesses closer to home via the alluring pastries, cakes and sarnies on offer – all sourced from local suppliers.

ESTABLISHED
2012

KEY ROASTER
Origin Coffee Roasters

BREWING METHOD
Espresso, AeroPress, cold brew, batch brew

MACHINE
La Marzocco Linea PB

GRINDER
Mahlkonig EK 43, Mahlkonig Tanzania, Nuova Simonelli Mythos

OPENING HOURS
Mon-Fri
7am-6.30pm
Sat 7.30am-6.30pm
Sun 9am-6pm

Gluten FREE

BEANS AVAILABLE INSTORE

ALTERNATIVE MILK

WIFI

CYCLE FRIENDLY

OUTDOOR seating

FAMILY FRIENDLY

DISABLED ACCESS

BRING YOUR OWN Cup.

---

www.society-cafe.com T: 01225 442433

f Society Cafe 🐦 @societycafe 📷 @societycafe

MAP 49. MOKOKO COFFEE – SOUTHGATE

7 Dorchester Street, Southgate, Bath, BA1 1SS

Swing by Mokoko's central set-up for a neighbourhood coffee bar experience loved by the locals – most of whom the baristas know by name.

It may be friendly but it's also serious about good coffee, and the caffeine crew can be seen at work through the picture windows, bringing a touch of theatre to the daily grind.

INSIDER'S TIP GRAB A BAG OF MOKOKO ROAST BEANS TO BREW AT HOME

It's a team with fine-tuned knowledge: these guys like nothing more than to experiment, exploring different coffees and roasts. There's always something new happening, such as this year's introduction of reverse osmosis, which results in a clearer and more consistent cup.

Coffee novices needn't be scared off though, as Mokoko aims to take the mystery out of coffee and to share the love. Be enlightened, surprised and entertained. If you need further persuasion, there's also a great selection of cakes and pastries, made at its sister coffee shop and bakery in Bristol.

ESTABLISHED
2014

KEY ROASTER
Mokoko,
La Cabra,
James Gourmet
Coffee

BREWING METHOD
Espresso, pourover

MACHINE
Conti Monte
Carlo

GRINDER
Mahlkonig K30 twin,
Mahlkonig EK 43

OPENING HOURS
Mon-Sat 7am-6pm
Sun 9am-6pm

Gluten FREE

BEANS AVAILABLE INSTORE

ALTERNATIVE MILK

WIFI

CYCLE FRIENDLY

OUTDOOR SEATING

DISABLED ACCESS

---

www.mokokocoffee.com   T: 01225 333444

f Mokoko Coffee   🐦 @mokokocoffee   📷 @mokokocoffee

MAP.º 50. THE RIVER HOUSE

7 The Bridge, Frome, Somerset, BA11 1AR

The coffee buffs at Somerset's most eccentric cafe have taken their dedication to the brew to the next level this year by roasting and serving their own beans.

Cooking up some bright and pleasing Guatemalan single origins under their Loud Mouth pseudonym, River House's crop of beans join Dusty Ape's sumptuous Silverback blend as a zesty canvas for the guys' serious latte art skills.

'I'm learning on the job,' says head roaster Anna. 'A course at London School of Coffee with Phil from Yallah nailed the basics and now I'm experimenting with some seriously fruity Guatemalan green beans. I can't get enough of the orangey tones.'

INSIDER'S TIP
HOT CHOC LOVERS WILL WANT A THREE WAY – AN EPIC MIX OF DARK, MILK AND WHITE REAL CHOC

The gluten-free syrups lavished on the lattes are also now crafted in-house – try the Himalayan sea salted caramel or vegan-friendly chai – in tune with the homemade breakfast, brunch and lunch haul.

Seasonally switched-up dishes (we're all over the badass benedict: potato and parmesan rosti, poached egg, crispy bacon and mustard cream) are served with a side of good vibes.

ESTABLISHED
2014

KEY ROASTER
Loud Mouth Coffee

BREWING METHOD
Espresso, cold brew

MACHINE
Astoria Plus 4 You

GRINDER
La Cimbali Magnum

OPENING HOURS
Mon-Fri
8am-6pm
Sat 9am-6pm
Sun 10am-4pm

Gluten FREE

BEANS AVAILABLE INSTORE

ALTERNATIVE MILK

WIFI

CYCLE FRIENDLY

OUTDOOR seating

DISABLED ACCESS

www.riverhousefrome.co.uk   T: 01373 464847

f The River House   🐦 @riverhousefrome   📷 @riverhousefrome

MAP № 51. MOO AND TWO

27 Catherine Hill, Frome, Somerset, BA11 1BY

It's not often that tea gets us quite as excited as coffee, but we're making an exception for Frome's loose-leaf alchemist.

Making an annual trip to India to source organic whole leaves to import, blend and sell from the Catherine Hill coffee shop, Moo and Two's founder Euan Barker creates a cache of infusions to be savoured at the wood-clad cafe or brewed at home.

INSIDER'S TIP FEEL FREE TO TAKE ALONG YOUR OWN VINYL TO SPIN ON THE RECORD PLAYER

With such care poured into the tisanes, the coffee is, naturally, crafted to an equally high standard. Round Hill's blend for Break Fluid Coffee Co provides a stunning starting point for Moo's baristas to create enticing espresso and full-bodied filters, alongside seasonal single origins from the Somerset roaster served via V60 or AeroPress.

Evening supper clubs, live music events and multimedia exhibitions expand Moo and Two's spectrum of delights, while the small batch coffee – including homemade cold brew – and house-blended teas can be found on the road via the roaming trailer.

ESTABLISHED
2016

KEY ROASTER
Round Hill Roastery

BREWING METHOD
Espresso, V60, AeroPress, cold brew

MACHINE
La Spaziale S5

GRINDER
Mazzer Super Jolly

OPENING HOURS
Tue-Sat
9am-5pm

---

www.mooandtwo.com   T: 07816 311452

f Moo and Two   🐦 @moo_and_two   📷 @mooandtwo

MAP №52. STRANGERS WITH COFFEE

31 St Cuthbert Street, Wells, Somerset, BA5 2AW

The many stages of planting, cultivating, picking, processing, shipping and roasting beans requires time and care, and it's a journey from crop to cup which Wells' original speciality coffee house pays homage to.

On this last step in the journey, barista and owner Ivan Hewitt handles the beans with the appreciation required to extract their full potential. Having trained with Origin and AllPress, he is an expert in his craft and it shows in the artful pour.

INSIDER'S TIP
BRING A TAKEAWAY CUP TO BAG A DISCOUNT ON COFFEE TO-GO

Don't let this intimidate you though: Strangers with Coffee is renowned for its friendly service, and Ivan delights in imparting his specialist knowledge to customers.

While the coffee is exceptionally good, the husband and wife team are no strangers to great food. A trained chef, Susan carefully matches the dishes they serve to complement the brews. Featuring only the best locally sourced products on the concise menu, the Hewitts' hens' organic eggs are used to create the showstopping range of counter bakes.

ESTABLISHED
2012

KEY ROASTER
AllPress Espresso

BREWING METHOD
Espresso, V60, pourover, syphon, cold brew, nitro

MACHINE
La Marzocco Linea

GRINDER
Mazzer Kony, Super Jolly, Vario

OPENING HOURS
Tue-Sat
7.30am-4pm

T: 07728 047233

f Strangers with Coffee

MAP№ 53. YEO VALLEY HQ
Rhodyate, Blagdon, Somerset, BS40 7YE

It's the home of some of the best organic milk in the country, so it makes absolute sense that Yeo Valley would only dose it with coffee that did it justice.

What's more surprising, however, is to find a canteen of this funky fabulousness in the wilds of the Somerset countryside. Because in addition to coffee, it's also made a name for itself as a dining destination of the hearty and rustic home cooking variety (tip: visit on a Wednesday for the own-reared roast – swoon).

INSIDER'S TIP POP-UP DINNERS ARE SOUGHT-AFTER AFFAIRS – LOOK OUT FOR UPCOMING DATES

Hooking up with excellent Bristol roaster Extract, Yeo Valley HQ has applied the same focus on quality to its coffee as it does to everything else, so as well as getting a decent americano at the end of lunch, the canteen is also a busy go-to for flat whites at elevenses.

Choose between espresso based brews, filter or french press and (it goes without saying) accompany it with a hunk of homemade cake – the coffee and walnut is especially drool-worthy.

ESTABLISHED
2015

KEY ROASTER
Extract Coffee Roasters

BREWING METHOD
Espresso, filter, french press

MACHINE
S5 Compact ED

GRINDER
Mazzer Lux

OPENING HOURS
Mon-Fri
8.30am-4.30pm

Gluten FREE

WiFi

CYCLE FRIENDLY

OUTDOOR SEATING

DISABLED ACCESS

---

www.yeovalley.co.uk   T: 01761 461677
f Yeo Valley   🐦 @yeovalley   📷 @yeovalley

№54. CALM COFFEE BAR

62 High Street, Burnham-on-Sea, Somerset, TA8 1PE

Channelling the 'healthy body, healthy mind' mantra, Calm Coffee Bar combines a sustainable mission and wellness ethos with top-notch barista artistry.

From reusable straws and compostable cups to gardening with coffee grounds and a ban on plastic bottles, you're assured of a clean, green conscience after imbibing a brew at this Burnham-on-Sea bolthole.

Bristol coffee roaster Extract provides 100 per cent ethically sourced beans, and its popular seasonal espressos such as Unkle Funka and Strong Man are available as alternatives to the house blend. Edible indulgences are similarly sin free, with a haul of organic goodies stocking the menu of handmade, gluten-free and refined sugar-free cakes.

INSIDER'S TIP
BYO REUSABLE MUG TO NAB A 10 PER CENT DISCOUNT ON YOUR BREW

Wellbeing classes held in the upstairs studio further cultivate the coffee shop's aura of calm. Head up the spiral staircase for body-and-mind-honing yoga and pilates.

And after all that stretching, give your jaw and stomach a workout with a hearty slice of chocolate and matcha cake with an espresso protein shake on the side.

ESTABLISHED
2015

KEY ROASTER
Extract Coffee Roasters

BREWING METHOD
Espresso

MACHINE
La Marzocco

GRINDER
Mahlkonig K30, Sanremo SR50

OPENING HOURS
Mon-Fri
8am-5pm
Sat
9am-5pm

 Gluten FREE

 BEANS AVAILABLE INSTORE

 ALTERNATIVE MILK

 WIFI

 CYCLE FRIENDLY

 FAMILY FRIENDLY

 DISABLED ACCESS

 BRING YOUR OWN Cup

www.calmcoffeebar.com
f Calm 🐦 @calmcoffeebar 📷 @calmcoffeebar

MAP № 55. FINCA

11 High Street, Yeovil, Somerset, BA20 1RG

This perfect little coffee shop in the centre of Yeovil is a very lucky find for local coffee lovers. Amid all the usual chains in this small town, it's rather thrilling to find a cafe that's consistently serving 90+ grade single origin coffees crafted at its own Dorchester roastery.

Whether you choose espresso, V60, AeroPress, cold brew or even (in summer) black tonic, there's no doubt that Finca is a veritable coffee sanctuary in a world of tastebud-stripping caramel lattes.

INSIDER'S TIP THE TEAM HAS JUST INTRODUCED ITS OWN RANGE OF SPECIALITY LONG LEAF TEAS

In addition, slabs of hearty handcrafted bakes – of the toasted banana bread, fig slice and salted caramel brownie variety – tick all the right boxes, leaving new converts feeling smug to have discovered this gem.

If you're a local, lucky you. If not, make it your Somerset detour to experience the happy vibe and soul sustaining pleasure that comes from excellent coffee and lovely homemade treats in jolly surroundings.

ESTABLISHED
2016

KEY ROASTER
Finca Coffee Roasters

BREWING METHOD
Espresso, V60, AeroPress, cold brew

MACHINE
La Marzocco

GRINDER
Olympus, Mazzer

OPENING HOURS
Mon-Sat
8am-4pm
Sun 10am-2pm

Gluten FREE

BEANS AVAILABLE INSTORE

ALTERNATIVE MILK

OUTDOOR seating

DISABLED ACCESS

COFFEE COURSES

---

www.fincacoffee.co.uk   T: 01305 300400

f Finca Yeovil   🐦 @scouting4coffee   📷 @scouting4coffee

MAP№ 56. SHOREDITCH WHITE

Corporation Street, Taunton, Somerset, TA1 4AW

Named after a local apple variety as opposed to the hip London neighbourhood, Shoreditch White was one of the first coffee shops to introduce speciality to Taunton.

Inspired to add a shot of contemporary cafe culture to Somerset's county town, Mark Tutton opened the spacious venue in 2016, plumping for local Brazier beans to ensure the coffee hit city standards.

A year on and the roaster's Altitude blend still stocks Shoreditch's grinder, and is crafted into silky flat whites and creamy cappuccinos via espresso.

INSIDER'S TIP POSH UP YOUR NEXT PLANNING MEETING WITH A SHOREDITCH WHITE CATERED BUFFET

Perfect poachies, Welsh rarebit with streaky bacon and black pudding, and chorizo hash make sticking around for brunch a tempting option. Beware spending too long over your brew and brunch though or the board of warm ciabatta rolls and lunchtime specials – crayfish cocktail sandwich and hot halloumi and pepper relish salad, for example – will persuade you to stay on for your next meal.

Just nipping in for a quick hit? Grab a carby treat from the counter such as an Oreo fudge brownie.

ESTABLISHED
2016

KEY ROASTER
Brazier Coffee Roasters

BREWING METHOD
Espresso

MACHINE
La Spaziale

GRINDER
Mazzer

OPENING HOURS
Mon-Sat
8am-3pm

---

www.shoreditchwhite.com   T: 01823 279977

f Shoreditch White   🐦 @shoreditchwh1   📷 @shoreditchwhite

BATH & SOMERSET

ROASTERS

200

NONETER 250

300

350

C

57. BRAZIER COFFEE ROASTERS

Unit 10, Tonedale Mill Business Park, Wellington, Somerset, TA21 0AW

Within a 19th century red brick building in the medieval town of Wellington, workers once produced miles of cloth for World War I.

Nowadays, Puttee House is home to pioneering coffee roasters, Brazier, which has breathed new life into the institution.

With regular inspiration coming from owner Claire's native Australia, she and husband Tom continue to steer the business and bring an antipodean influence to this corner of Somerset.

In order to cater to a surge in wholesale customers, they've upped sticks to larger premises this year. The move has not only increased their bean roasting capabilities, it's allowed them to welcome local coffee drinkers keen to learn more about speciality coffee to their on-site cafe.

LOOK OUT FOR WEEKEND OPENING HOURS AND A SMALL BUT PERFECTLY FORMED BRUNCH AND LUNCH MENU COMING SOON

Visit to experience Brazier's flagship roast, Altitude, a smooth caramel blend achieved by seeking out some of the hardest to reach green beans. Sister blends Latitude and Longitude offer more rich, nutty roasts for the burgeoning home brewer.

ESTABLISHED
2015

ROASTER
MAKE & SIZE
Giesen W6A

CAFE ONSITE

OPEN TO THE PUBLIC

COFFEE COURSES

CUPPING EVENTS

BEANS AVAILABLE
ONSITE
ONLINE

www.braziercoffeeroasters.co.uk   T: 01823 666585

f Brazier Coffee Roasters   🐦 @brazierroasters   📷 @braziercoffeeroasters

WILTSHIRE & DORSET

LEYKERS
#59

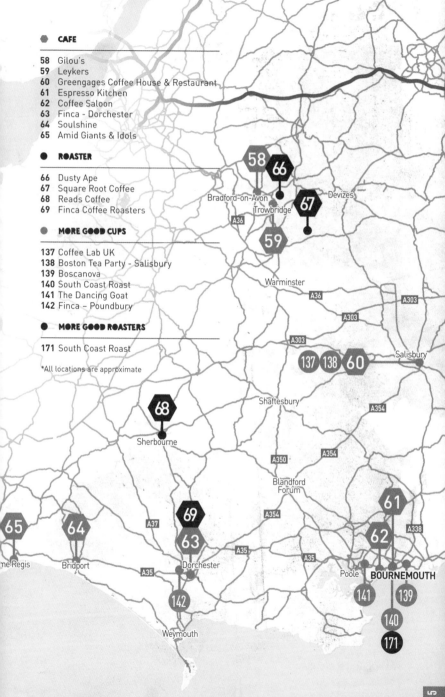

*All locations are approximate

MAP№ 58. GILOU'S

4 The Shambles, Bradford on Avon, Wiltshire, BA15 1JS

With cobbled streets full of antique shops, galleries, gift shops and pretty homes with climbing flowers, the picture-postcard town of Bradford on Avon is a pocket-sized wonderland.

After a day of exploring, look for Gilou's, a charming cafe off Silver Street. Half of the charm comes from Gilou himself – a French, classically-trained baker and chef with the heart of a foodie.

His adoration of baking shines through in stacks of buttery brioche, flaky pastries and homemade delights. With locally sourced specials penned onto the windows, this cafe wouldn't seem out of place in a French provincial town.

INSIDER'S TIP COSY UP ON THE CHESTERFIELD WITH A CREAMY FLAT WHITE AND GOAT'S CHEESE TARTINE

Gilou is equally passionate about coffee and will only buy single origin beans, often through Round Hill Roastery and Origin. 'As a chef, I give all credit to the farmers. It's the same with coffee, it's the growers that make all the difference.'

Gilou prepares espresso, filter brews and coffee based cocktails, but for theatrics and a clean profile we'd recommend the thrills of the syphon.

ESTABLISHED
2016

KEY ROASTER
Round Hill Roastery, Origin Coffee Roasters

BREWING METHOD
Espresso, AeroPress, V60, syphon

MACHINE
Sanremo Zoe

GRINDER
Mythos One, Mazzer

OPENING HOURS
Thu-Sat
10am-8pm
Sun-Mon
10am-4pm

 Gluten FREE

 BEANS AVAILABLE INSTORE

 ALTERNATIVE MILK

 WIFI

 CYCLE FRIENDLY

 OUTDOOR Seating

 FAMILY FRIENDLY

DISABLED ACCESS

---

www.gilouscafe.com   T: 01225 862203

f Gilou's @gilouscafe

MAP 59. LEYKERS

1 White Hart Yard, Trowbridge, Wiltshire, BA14 8BY

Following a major refit in spring 2017, Leykers flung open its doors to reveal a revamped and rebranded new cafe experience for its regulars.

New additions include a Trowbridge-inspired wall mural, a gorgeously greedy extended menu, Peroni on tap and space for over a hundred caffeine fiends to get cosy with a carefully poured coffee.

INSIDER'S TIP GRAB A LOYALTY CARD TO GAIN POINTS FOR COFFEE AND TO DONATE TO LOCAL CHARITIES

Fellow Wiltshire warrior Dusty Ape continues to fill the Mahlkonig grinder with beans to savour as you sink into one of the squidgy armchairs. Then follow your espresso based brew with a board piled high with antipasti.

Delicious coffee and food aren't the only things drawing in the punters; husband and wife team Tracy and Graham Parker have got a new alcohol licence and have put late opening hours in place so they can host evening sessions.

Let your mocha morph into malbec as you stick around to enjoy live music and the regular not-in-a-pub quiz.

ESTABLISHED
1999

KEY ROASTER
Dusty Ape

BREWING METHOD
Espresso

MACHINE
La Marzocco

GRINDER
Mahlkonig K30

OPENING HOURS
Mon-Wed
7am-5.30pm
Thu-Sat
7am-11pm
Sun 9am-4pm

---

www.leykers.co.uk T: 01225 768844

f Leykers 🐦 @coffee_central

MAP № 60. GREENGAGES COFFEE HOUSE & RESTAURANT

31 Catherine Street, Salisbury, Wiltshire, SP1 2DQ

Greengages continues its happy marriage of excellent coffee and a wide foodie offering at this neighbourhood cafe which serves a broad range of customers.

Bean geeks will love the ground floor with its coffee sack covered bench and espresso machine in the middle of the action, so they can sip their exceedingly good Round Hill roasts to the sizzle of the steam wand.

Coffee is taken very seriously here, and experienced baristas provide all important consistency in the serving of beans from one of the South West's most exciting roasteries.

INSIDER'S TIP ALL COFFEE SERVED IS SINGLE ORIGIN AND DIRECTLY SOURCED BY ROUND HILL

Upstairs sees busy waiting staff bustling around, delivering plates of good home cooking to a thronging horde of regulars.

The vegan options are vast and ever increasing. A lot of attention is paid to gluten-free and other dietary restrictions too, so customers can relax knowing they're in good hands at this welcoming setting.

ESTABLISHED
2012

KEY ROASTER
Round Hill Roastery

BREWING METHOD
Espresso, drip, cafetiere, Clever Dripper, AeroPress, filter

MACHINE
La Marzocco Linea PB

GRINDER
Mahlkonig EK 43

OPENING HOURS
Mon-Sat
8am-5pm

Gluten FREE

BEANS AVAILABLE INSTORE

ALTERNATIVE MILK

WIFI

CYCLE FRIENDLY

OUTDOOR seating

FAMILY FRIENDLY

DISABLED ACCESS

---

www.greengagessalisbury.co.uk   T: 01722 349934

f Greengages Coffeehouse & Restaurant

№61. ESPRESSO KITCHEN

69 Commercial Road, The Triangle, Bournemouth, Dorset, BH2 5RT

This vibrant hub in the heart of Bournemouth has upped its coffee game this year, adding almond and soya to its bill of alternatives and trading in the Mazzer grinder for a swish new La Marzocco.

Benefitting from the new arrivals is a selection of South West roasted, organic coffees which are worked into glossy espresso by owner Francesca Silvestre. The house blend from Dorset's Beanpress makes a killer almond cortado, while the week's single origin from a line-up of guest roasters serves those who favour filter.

INSIDER'S TIP FOLLOW THE CROWD AND ORDER A FLAT WHITE WITH A WEDGE OF HOMEMADE CARROT CAKE

Whether you go black or white, Francesca's background in design means you'll be sipping in bright and beautiful surroundings. Downstairs, cheese graters replace lamp shades, surf boards dangle from the ceiling and vintage newspapers decorate the walls. Upstairs, meanwhile, is a hidey-hole of fairylights, rabbit-printed bunting and colouring books.

The homemade, organic, vegan-friendly fodder is just as colourful. Follow the daily toastie special – faves include roasted veg grilled cheese – with a slice of something indulgent from the impressive cake collection.

ESTABLISHED
2012

KEY ROASTER
Beanpress Coffee Co.

BREWING METHOD
Espresso

MACHINE
La Marzocco FB70

GRINDER
La Marzocco Swift

OPENING HOURS
Mon-Sat
7am-7pm
Sun 10am-6pm

www.espressokitchen.co.uk T: 01202 972420

f Espresso Kitchen Bournemouth 🐦 @expressokitchen 📷 @espressokitchen

MAP 62. COFFEE SALOON

62 Seamoor Road, Westbourne, Bournemouth, BH4 9AS

Photo: Matt Hardy Photography

Speciality coffee continues to proliferate across the south coast thanks, in part, to the stable of espresso-slinging baristas at The Coffee Saloon's five outposts.

The latest Wild West-inspired coffee shop to join the clan is yet again taking on the high street corporates and waving the tamper for speciality and independence.

Longstanding roaster Origin is backing the indie coffee house in this showdown, stocking its grinders with top-notch Cornwall-roasted beans. They're then fashioned into a stonking selection of milk-based brews on a gorgeous matt black customised Strava AV 3 group with wooden trim (swoon).

INSIDER'S TIP THE CHOC ORANGE BROWNIES – BAKED AT THE CANFORD CLIFFS SALOON – ARE NEXT LEVEL

Like its sister venues, upcycled furniture and vintage design create a unique and quirky space in which to sit and sip, while communal-style seating encourages brunch-goers and cake-munchers to interact over a cracking cup of coffee.

ESTABLISHED
2014

KEY ROASTER
Origin Coffee Roasters

BREWING METHOD
Espresso

MACHINE
La Marzocco Strada AV custom 3 group

GRINDER
Nuova Simonelli Mythos One

OPENING HOURS
Mon-Fri
7am-4pm
Sat 8am-5pm
Sun 9am-3pm

---

www.coffeesaloon.com T: 01929 552416

f Coffee Saloon @thecoffeesaloons

MAP № 63. FINCA

41 Great Western Road, Dorchester, Dorset, DT1 1UF

The original Dorchester speciality coffee shop, Finca is a fab find for own-roasted, top-notch coffee served in a relaxed environment which is all wood and cheer.

Rustic interiors are complemented by friendly staff, oozing toasties and hunks of homemade cakes, including raw, vegan and gluten-free options.

In summer the bi-fold windows open to let the sun in, and local caffeine fiends make a beeline for outdoor seating, nitro (the only place serving it for miles) and the juicy cold brew.

Originally this was the site of the Finca roastery, but that's moved to a bigger site on The Grove where its new 10kg Toper batch roaster is doing the honours with 80+ (and often 90+) SCA graded coffees.

INSIDER'S TIP VISIT IN SUMMER TO SIP NITRO AND COLD BREW IN THE SUN

As a result, the cafe has a regularly changing array of single origins available to taste, so customers can explore the full spectrum of different flavours as well as experimenting with a range of serve styles. Look out for a third shop opening at The Buttercross in Poundbury.

ESTABLISHED
2014

KEY ROASTER
Finca Coffee
Roasters

BREWING METHOD
Espresso, V60,
AeroPress,
nitro, cold brew

MACHINE
La Marzocco

GRINDER
Olympus,
Mazzer

OPENING HOURS
Mon-Sat
9am-4pm
Sun 10am-2pm

 Gluten FREE

 BEANS AVAILABLE INSTORE

 ALTERNATIVE MILK

 OUTDOOR seating

 DISABLED ACCESS

 COFFEE COURSES

www.fincacoffee.co.uk   T: 01305 300400

f Finca Dorchester   🐦 @scouting4coffee   📷 @scouting4coffee

№64. SOULSHINE

76 South Street, Bridport, Dorset, DT6 3NN

Push through the doors of Soulshine and you'll be enveloped by a sunny, gently spiced air – the perfect marriage of coffee and baking bread.

Chris Denne and Lisa Loader have created a nirvana complete with squashy leather sofas, long communal tables, and a sunny courtyard set among herbs and blooms.

The menu is something to behold: large bowls piled high with wholesome salads in summer and warming soups in winter. With animal welfare, sustainability and the local community high on the agenda, brunch-goers and visiting veggies can tuck into ethically sourced and organic grub with a green conscience.

INSIDER'S TIP CHECK SOCIAL MEDIA FOR UPCOMING BARBECUE, ITALIAN AND LIVE MUSIC EVENINGS

Understandably, the Soulshine crowd are fussy about who they source their coffee from. They champion independent roasters like Extract in Bristol who, in turn, are equally fussy about sourcing their beans and ensuring growers receive more than Fairtrade prices. They also sell reusable cups and straws.

ESTABLISHED
2014

KEY ROASTER
Extract Coffee Roasters

BREWING METHOD
Espresso, AeroPress

MACHINE
Sanremo Verona TCS

GRINDER
Mahlkonig K30 Vario Air, Sanremo SR50

OPENING HOURS
Mon-Sat
9am-4pm
Sun 10am-2pm

Gluten FREE
BEANS AVAILABLE INSTORE
ALTERNATIVE MILK
WIFI
CYCLE FRIENDLY
OUTDOOR Seating
FAMILY Friendly
DISABLED ACCESS
BRING YOUR OWN Cup

www.soulshinecafe.co.uk   T: 01308 422821

f Soulshine Cafe   🐦 @soulshinecafe   📷 @soulshinecafe

Nº 65. AMID GIANTS & IDOLS

59 Silver Street, Lyme Regis, Dorset, DT7 3HR

Tucked away on Silver Street is a much-loved speciality coffee house, a relaxing oasis close to the centre of Lyme Regis.

The revered Dorset coffee shop is a bean-lover's haven where shoppers can rest their feet, catch their breath and fortify themselves with great coffee.

As well as serving its own-roasted house blend Coast, owners Elaine and Steve work with local roasteries including Exeter's Crankhouse and Somerset's Brazier Coffee to offer a variety of single estate beans served as espresso or expertly filtered AeroPress, V60 and Woodneck.

INSIDER'S TIP LIKE WHAT YOU'RE DRINKING? PICK UP A BAG OF THE COAST HOUSE BLEND TO BREW AT HOME

Squashy leather armchairs, a variety of board games and packs of jokes make this dog-friendly cafe somewhere to hunker down with friends after a stomp on the nearby South West Coast Path.

There's more than outstanding coffee too – daily specials and soups provide post-walk sustenance, while a bounty of homemade bakes offer a well-earned sugar fix.

ESTABLISHED
2014

KEY ROASTER
Amid Giants & Idols

BREWING METHOD
Espresso, AeroPress, V60, Woodneck

MACHINE
La Marzocco Linea

GRINDER
Mazzer

OPENING HOURS
Mon-Sun
10am-4pm

---

www.amidgiantsandidols.co.uk   T: 07779 794381

ROASTERS

WILTSHIRE & DORSET

SQUARE
ROOT
COFFEE
#67

KINGSMEAD
BLEND

MEXICAN

ETHIOPIAN
YIRGACHEFFE

£7.95

66. DUSTY APE

Marsh Farm Roastery, Hilperton, Wiltshire, BA14 7PJ

Since last year's guide, the gang at Dusty Ape have been on a caffeinated mission to grow, improve and invest. And boy, are they ticking off the boxes.

After expanding the roastery, installing a second roaster, increasing the number of staff and introducing pukka new packaging, Ape's capacity has almost tripled, making this its busiest year to date.

The impressive line-up of single origins – underpinned by the well loved, full bodied Molten Toffee and Silverback blends – is joined by guests including a delicately-flavoured addition called Gyawali Mandalay, which scooped Best Washed Coffee from Myanmar 2017.

'WE'VE INVESTED IN NEW, HIGH END EQUIPMENT TO REALLY MAKE OUR COFFEES SING'

The award winning squad don't spend all their time roasting though – developing knowledge and educating others in all things speciality is also key: *'We openly share our learning so customers get maximum enjoyment from our coffees,'* say the guys.

From distributing Sanremo machines to offering engineering services and training courses, they ensure they're not the only ones going bananas (sorry) for beans.

ESTABLISHED
2013

ROASTER
MAKE & SIZE
Probat 12kg,
Toper TKMSX
5kg

OPEN
BY APPOINTMENT

OPEN
TO THE PUBLIC

COFFEE
COURSES

CUPPING
EVENTS

BEANS
AVAILABLE
ONSITE
ONLINE

www.dustyape.com   T: 01225 753838
f Dusty Ape   🐦 @dustyape   📷 @dustyape

MAP 67. SQUARE ROOT COFFEE
12 Station Yard, Edington, Wiltshire, BA13 4NT

Exploring the alchemy of beans, uncovering the magic of roasting, savouring the marvels of different brew methods: it's no wonder Adrian Smith felt an irresistible attraction towards roasting.

Delving into a world beyond the cup, the now master roaster realised the potential to create immense complexity of flavour, aroma and sweetness ... and the rest, as they say, is history.

'EVERY ROAST IS SAMPLED IN OUR CUPPING ROOM TO MAKE SURE THAT THE TASTE PROFILE IS EXACTLY AS PLANNED'

Since then, Square Root has gone from strength to strength. A recent move to Station Yard in picturesque Wiltshire surroundings, has provided inspiration and space to house beloved Turkish handbuilt drum roaster, Laura (she never roasts a bigger batch than 3kg). Adrian has also been perfecting smooth, no-bitterness signature blend The Solution with its beautiful Brazilian-Indian-Sumatran bean ensemble.

There ain't no sitting still at Square Root: *'Coffee is a seasonal crop, and we are constantly on the lookout for the most amazing beans that we then extensively profile roast to find the sweet spot. Only then do we bring it to you,'* enthuses Adrian.

ESTABLISHED
2015

ROASTER
MAKE & SIZE
Custom Turkish
TX5 5kg

OPEN
BY APPOINTMENT

COFFEE COURSES

BEANS AVAILABLE

ONLINE

---

www.squarerootcoffee.com T: 07940 120835
f Square Root Coffee 🐦 @sqrootcoffee

MAP: 68. READS COFFEE

Limekiln Farm, Thornford Road, Sherborne, Dorset, DT9 6PS

Building on its growing success in recent years, Reads is pushing forward to ensure its service is as sensational as the award winning espresso blends it proudly produces: *'We've been busy investing in making the roastery run super smoothly,'* explains Giles, who founded the roastery with his wife Charlotte in 2001.

More haybarn than hipster (and thoroughly charming for it), the roastery operates from an idyllic Dorset location on the site of a converted dairy. This family affair sees Giles heading up the roasting, while Charlotte runs the office and packing room with an enthusiastic team of local bean-atics.

'THERE'S MORE TO LATTE THAN ART,' SAYS GILES

Reads aims to provide a meticulous service to make sure its customers have all they need to create the perfect cup: *'We work extremely closely with our commercial and retail customers to ensure they have the right machines, brewing kit, proper training and support material.'*

Sourcing new origins from across the globe, including exceptional decafs, the Reads team want to provide the perfect roast to please every palate: *'We aim to offer something for everyone, whether it's a light, bright, fruity African or a full-on dark roast Indonesian groundshaker.'*

ESTABLISHED
2001

ROASTER
MAKE & SIZE
Probat 25kg,
Ambex 12kg

OPEN
TO THE PUBLIC

COFFEE
COURSES

CUPPING
EVENTS

BEANS
AVAILABLE

www.readscoffee.co.uk   T: 01935 481010

f Reads Coffee Roasters   🐦 @reads_coffee   📷 @readscoffeeroasters

DEVELOPED WITH BARISTAS FOR BARISTAS

- Perfect for latte art
- No added sugar
- Cholesterol free, low fat alternative to milk
- 30% less calories than skimmed & regular soy milk

UNSWEETENED

BLUE DIAMOND
ALMONDS

Almond Breeze

Serving Suggestion

Rich & Creamy

BARISTA BLEND
Created for Use by Professionals
Dairy and Soya Free

Baristas know their coffee better than anyone. That's why we got baristas to help us make ou
new, low calorie Almond Breeze® Barista Blend. It's deliciously creamy and frothy, making it perfect fo
the world's finest coffee. And because it's an almond drink, it's dairy free and soya fre

For more information & stockists visit **bluediamondalmonds.co.**

MAP 69. FINCA COFFEE ROASTERS

Unit 101, 20-22 The Grove, Dorchester, Dorset, DT1 1ST

This Dorchester roastery is the new HQ of the growing Finca coffee brand.

Taking little steps on the road to greatness, the team started roasting in small batches at their first cafe in 2014, committed to crafting only speciality grade beans of the highest quality.

First they provided coffees for their Dorchester outlet (along with seriously good bakes which are all made in-house). Then a couple of years later the team launched a sister coffee shop in Yeovil, which showcases the same regularly changing single origins and cracking cakes.

ESTABLISHED
2016

ROASTER
MAKE & SIZE
Toper TKMSX 10kg,
CBR-1200 1kg,
CBR-101 ¼kg

OPEN
BY APPOINTMENT

CUPPING
EVENTS

BEANS
AVAILABLE

ONSITE

FINCA ONLY ROAST SPECIALITY GRADE COFFEE THAT'S SCA 80+ AND GROWN AT HIGH ALTITUDE

The latest development has been the moving of the roastery to fresh premises on The Grove and the installation of a spanking 10kg small batch roaster, providing the impetus to supply other speciality coffee shops with single origins. The team have developed a speciality blend called High Altitude which is available through a local food distributor and an Estate Speciality Blend which is available directly from Finca.

The roastery can supply 90+ coffee in small batches for speciality cafes as guest coffees, as well as white labelling them for customers who want own-brand beans.

www.fincacoffee.co.uk   T: 01305 300400

f Finca Coffee Roasters   🐦 @fincacoffee   📷 @scouting4coffee

THE
HUTONG
CAFE #86

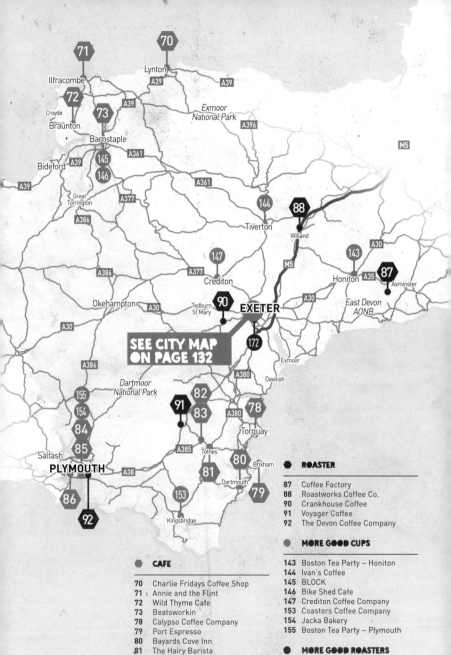

SEE CITY MAP
ON PAGE 132

SEE CITY MAP ON PAGE 132

ROASTER

87 Coffee Factory
88 Roastworks Coffee Co.
90 Crankhouse Coffee
91 Voyager Coffee
92 The Devon Coffee Company

MORE GOOD CUPS

143 Boston Tea Party – Honiton
144 Ivan's Coffee
145 BLOCK
146 Bike Shed Cafe
147 Crediton Coffee Company
153 Coasters Coffee Company
154 Jacka Bakery
155 Boston Tea Party – Plymouth

MORE GOOD ROASTERS

172 Littlestone Coffee

*All locations are approximate

CAFE

70 Charlie Fridays Coffee Shop
71 Annie and the Flint
72 Wild Thyme Cafe
73 Beatsworkin
78 Calypso Coffee Company
79 Port Espresso
80 Bayards Cove Inn
81 The Hairy Barista
82 Bayards Kitchen
83 The Almond Thief
84 Rockets & Rascals
85 The Mad Merchant Coffee House
86 The Hutong Cafe

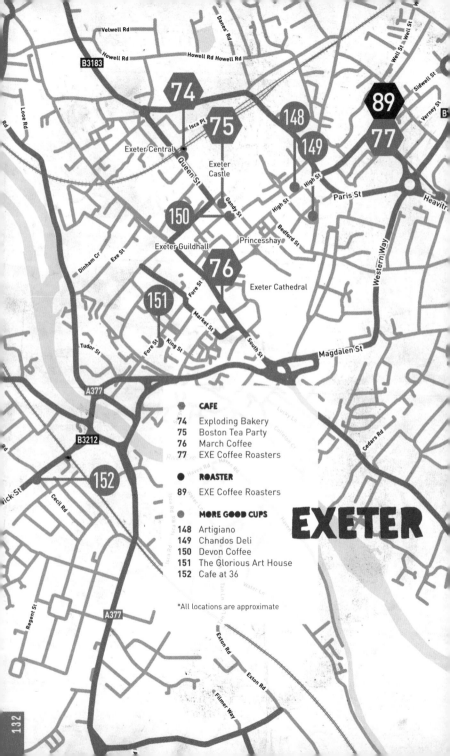

CAFE

74 Exploding Bakery
75 Boston Tea Party
76 March Coffee
77 EXE Coffee Roasters

ROASTER

89 EXE Coffee Roasters

MORE GOOD CUPS

148 Artigiano
149 Chandos Deli
150 Devon Coffee
151 The Glorious Art House
152 Cafe at 36

*All locations are approximate

EXETER

₌₇₀. CHARLIE FRIDAYS COFFEE SHOP

Church Steps, Queens Street, Lynton, Devon, EX35 6HY

Mismatched tables, fresh flowers, fairy lights, comfy cushions, candles and a joyous lime green wash lend Charlie Fridays its fun and funky atmosphere. Add to that games, colouring books, guitars, knitting and DJ nights and it's easy to see why regulars want to spend their downtime at this uplifting hangout.

A wishing gate adorned with customers' aspirations is an optimistic touch but you don't need to be wearing rose coloured specs for your coffee dreams to come true. Beans roasted by Bristol's Extract are served in various guises including espresso, macchiato and white or dark mocha.

INSIDER'S TIP THE CHINESE NIGHTS – BASED ON RECIPES FROM HUANG KITCHEN – ARE LEGENDARY

Quirky liquid refreshment comes in the form of affogatos, chai lattes and matcha chai. There are also tempting teas, hot chocolates and boozy tipples.

No need to fret if you're not doing meat, dairy or gluten, as there are tons of inventive free-from options on the bill of homemade curries, paninis, toasties and cakes. Locals go mad for the glorious waffle stack with bacon and maple syrup.

ESTABLISHED
2014

KEY ROASTER
Extract
Coffee Roasters

BREWING METHOD
Espresso,
cafetiere

MACHINE
Sanremo Zoe

GRINDER
Sanremo SR70

OPENING HOURS
Mon-Sun
10am-6pm
(reduced in
winter)

Gluten FREE

BEANS AVAILABLE INSTORE

ALTERNATIVE MILK

WIFI

FAMILY FRIENDLY

www.charliefridays.co.uk   T: 07544 123324

f charlie friday's coffee shop   🐦 @charliefridays   📷 @charliefridays

71. ANNIE AND THE FLINT

126 High Street, Ilfracombe, Devon, EX34 9EY

Pining for one that is rich, dark and handsome? Have a penchant for a medium body with a long sweet finish? Love a good looking flat white? Matchmakers Annie and the Flint can pair you with a suitable beau to ignite your senses. Carefully sourced beans, expertly roasted at Helston's Origin and served in espresso based drinks, are the perfect paramour.

But it's not just the coffee at this industrial-chic Ilfracombe haunt that inflames passion; it's also the health-conscious, fresh vibe of the food offering. From salads of roasted broccoli, pine nut and feta to pancake brekkies with yogurt, compote and berries, there is always something delicious and nutritious to try.

INSIDER'S TIP CAFFEINE OVERLOAD? TRY A CHAI, TURMERIC OR EARL GREY LATTE INSTEAD

Go on a superfood health kick with peanut butter energy truffles – stuffed with dates, coconut oil and oats – and a Purple Blast smoothie of blueberries, pomegranate and organic yogurt.

And if you want to re-create it all with your loved ones at home, grab a bag of beans and a jar of honey from the shop on the way out.

ESTABLISHED
2016

KEY ROASTER
Origin Coffee Roasters

BREWING METHOD
Espresso

MACHINE
La Marzocco

GRINDER
Mythos One

OPENING HOURS
Mon-Fri
8.30am-4.30pm
Sat
9am-4pm

Gluten FREE

BEANS AVAILABLE INSTORE

ALTERNATIVE MILK

WIFI

FAMILY FRIENDLY

DISABLED ACCESS

BRING YOUR OWN cup.

www.annieandtheflint.co.uk   T: 01271 866436

f Annie and the Flint   @annieandtheflint

MAP 72. WILD THYME CAFE

5 Caen Field Shopping Centre, Braunton, Devon, EX33 1EE

Just five minutes' drive from the famed longboard surf spot of Saunton beach, Wild Thyme is always packed out with smoothie-slurping, brunch-munching regulars on their way to catch some waves – or sandy and exhausted on their way home.

The espresso based drinks come courtesy of Bristol roaster Clifton in a longstanding collaboration that results in continuous training for the Thyme team.

INSIDER'S TIP TRY THE HARISSA VEGETABLES WITH COUSCOUS AND HUMMUS FOR A VERITABLE VEGGIE FEAST

Brekkie is big here: bacon sarnies, banana porridge and fresh fruit salad with granola, yogurt and honey are perfect to set you up for the surf. Later in the day, pair your brew with a find from the veggie and vegan-friendly menu (smoky chipotle bean chilli with corn fritters and rice is a winner) followed by a hunk of cake.

The squad is also now taking its foodie finesse to weddings, parties and festivals: hog roasting at hen dos, dishing up tapas in tents and barbecuing at birthday parties.

ESTABLISHED
2006

KEY ROASTER
Clifton Coffee
Roasters

BREWING METHOD
Espresso

MACHINE
Astoria Plus
4 You

GRINDER
Mazzer Super
Jolly Timer

OPENING HOURS
Mon-Sun
9am-4pm
(extended in
summer)

---

www.wildthymecafe.co.uk   T: 01271 815191

f Wild Thyme Cafe   🐦 @wildthymecafe   📷 @wildthymecafe

73. BEATSWORKIN

6 Queen's House, Queen's Street, Barnstaple, Devon, EX32 8HJ

A love of both the board and a decent brew make for a great mash-up at Glenn Field's caffeinated skate shop in Barnstaple.

With its polished concrete bar, exposed brickwork and vibrant skateboard-decked walls, it's the fresh and funky hangout for anyone with a passion for the grind – of both the skateboard and speciality coffee varieties.

INSIDER'S TIP HAVE A SUPERFOOD SPLURGE: TRY A HEMP, SPIRULINA AND BAOBAB SMOOTHIE

When it came to choosing a roaster for his urban joint, organic Beanberry coffee was the only choice for Glenn who has a passion for promoting sustainable living in every aspect of his business. Whether it's skating, music, clothing (he's got a streetwear shop two doors down) or coffee, everything comes with indie and green credentials.

Skaters looking to pull sweet tricks fuel themselves on oat and raw choccie bars, superfood smoothies and organic energy drinks. But skater or not, everyone's welcome and the wholesome cakes, friendly vibe and cracking coffee prepared as espresso, V60 or Chemex, are a big draw.

ESTABLISHED
2015

KEY ROASTER
Beanberry Coffee Company

BREWING METHOD
Espresso, V60, Chemex

MACHINE
Sanremo Verona TCS

GRINDER
Mahlkonig K30 Air

OPENING HOURS
Mon-Sat
9am-6pm
Sun
11am-4pm

T: 01271 321111
f Beatsworkin Coffee n Skate   @beatsworkinuk   @beatsworkin

MAP 74. EXPLODING BAKERY

1b Central Station, Queen Street, Exeter, Devon, EX4 3SB

It's worth catching an early train to Exeter to nab one of the city's best people-watching spots outside Exploding Bakery.

The communal benches next to Exeter Central station are a prime place to spy on city-slickers hot-footing it to the office with a 'spro in hand, or students snaffling a slab of cake for breakfast. But it's the view of the Exploding bakers working on the next batch of baked beauties that's the sweetest sight of all.

Inside the simply styled cafe, a new bakers' table offers voyeurs an even better snoop at what's going down in the kitchen. Usually it's the prep of a delicious array of lunch dishes and haul of scrumptious bakes to scoff in situ or pig out on later.

INSIDER'S TIP
THIS IS YOUR STOP FOR 'THE BEST MOTHER CLUCKING CAKE IN TOWN'

Expertly crafted coffee is a key part of the experience; whether you're sipping a carefully made single origin via Chemex or a well slung espresso lavished with foamy milk, the baristas make it look easy.

Beans are sourced from a number of roasters, including regional faves such as Crankhouse and Round Hill, along with speciality infusions from Postcard Teas.

ESTABLISHED
2011

KEY ROASTER
Square Mile
Coffee Roasters,
Crankhouse Coffee,
Round Hill
Roastery

BREWING METHOD
Espresso, V60,
Chemex,
AeroPress,
cold brew

MACHINE
La Marzocco
Linea Classic

GRINDER
Mythos One x 2

OPENING HOURS
Mon-Fri
8am-4pm
Sat 9am-4pm

---

www.explodingbakery.com   T: 01392 427900

f The Exploding Bakery   🐦 @explodingbakery   📷 @explodingbakery

№75. BOSTON TEA PARTY – EXETER

84 Queen Street, Exeter, Devon, EX4 3RP

Boston's Exeter branch may not look much from the outside but venture up the wooden staircase and you'll find a bazaar of brew-fuelled chat and cake-scoffing catch ups.

The huge, high-ceilinged dining room continues to be a haven for coffee lovers and keen foodies in the Cathedral city, where it feels part of the furniture after all these years.

Eschewing snobbery and embracing the opportunity to welcome the caffeine curious into the fold, the troop of tamper-tastic baristas are always happy to help with roast tips and recommendations.

Beans are supplied by the clever chaps at Extract, who ensure top quality South American beans fill the hopper. The Bristol roaster is so keen to buy the best that it sent a crack squad of bean geeks out to Colombia to build relationships with growers.

INSIDER'S TIP JOIN THE 'GOOD FOR NOTHING' GROUP AT BTP AND MAKE POSITIVE STUFF HAPPEN IN THE COMMUNITY

As well as phenomenal brews, the BTP crew whip up a storm in the kitchen. The Vietnamese bánh-mì sandwich is a fave: barbecue pulled jackfruit, pickled veg, coriander, vegan mayo and sriracha sauce in a toasted baguette with pickled coleslaw.

ESTABLISHED
1997

KEY ROASTER
Extract Coffee Roasters

BREWING METHOD
Espresso, filter

MACHINE
La Marzocco Linea Classic

GRINDER
Mazzer Major

OPENING HOURS
Mon-Sun
7.30am-7pm

Gluten FREE

BEANS AVAILABLE INSTORE

ALTERNATIVE MILK

WIFI

CYCLE FRIENDLY

OUTDOOR SEATING

FAMILY FRIENDLY

BRING YOUR OWN CUP.

---

www.bostonteaparty.co.uk   T: 01392 201181

f Boston Tea Party Cafés   🐦 @btpcafes   📷 @btpcafes

MAP 76. MARCH COFFEE

87 South Street, Exeter, Devon, EX1 1EQ

With a stripped back menu to match its contemporary industrial design, don't visit Exeter's latest speciality shop in search of lengthy lunch listings or a kaleidoscope of syrup-dosed coffees.

Instead, appreciate the complex flavours in the prudently poured Crankhouse espresso while chatting tasting notes with owner and barista John Petherick. You'll find the Exeter roaster's current beans chalked up on the blackboard behind the bar, with occasional guest roasts from notable names such as Caravan, along with a nitro offering from Frank and Ernest.

INSIDER'S TIP LOOK OUT FOR EVENING CUPPING SESSIONS WITH LOCAL ROASTER CRANKHOUSE

March's signature handmade doughnuts – matcha green tea, passion fruit and coffee cream are all big hits – keep sugar levels spiked until the brunch menu comes into force later this year. There's also a small selection of stuffed sarnies, bejewelled granola bars and gooey brownies at the counter to keep coffee fans well fed.

Plans to add an EK 43 to the armoury in autumn 2017 will expand John's current coffee offering – keep an eye open for filter options and new names on the board.

ESTABLISHED
2017

KEY ROASTER
Crankhouse Coffee

BREWING METHOD
Espresso, nitro cold brew

MACHINE
La Marzocco Strada

GRINDER
Mythos One

OPENING HOURS
Tue-Fri
8am-6pm
Sat 9am-6pm
Sun 10am-4pm

Gluten FREE

BEANS AVAILABLE INSTORE

ALTERNATIVE MILK

WIFI

www.marchcoffee.co.uk   T: 07972 694606

f March coffee   🐦 @marchcoffeeexe   📷 @marchcoffeeexeter

77. EXE COFFEE ROASTERS

19 Heavitree Road, Exeter, Devon, EX1 2LD

Photo: Matt Austin

It's been a labour of love and a long journey for Steve and Kim Pearson of Exeter's first coffee shop and roastery hybrid.

Starting out on the festival circuit in 2004, The Pearson's foray into caffeine kicked off with a custom converted coffee van. As their passion grew, so did their following, and in 2012 they opened Devon Coffee on Queen Street. Three years later, Steve set about building his own gas flame drum roaster and was soon serving his hand-roasted coffee from a second outpost in the city.

INSIDER'S TIP
THIS IS YOUR WEEKEND HANGOUT FOR CHILLED BEVVIES AND STONE-BAKED PIZZA POP-UPS

Whatever's being pulled through the La Marzocco machine or filtered on the brew bar is roasted in the basement of this contemporary coffee stop. If the sun's out, grab a spot on the bench out front or head to the canopy-covered courtyard for alfresco sipping.

The seasonal selection of beans can be picked up in store for home brewing: the team also offer Be a Barista courses if you're keen to sharpen your speciality skills.

ESTABLISHED
2015

KEY ROASTER
Exe Coffee Roasters

BREWING METHOD
Espresso, V60, AeroPress, Chemex

MACHINE
La Marzocco PB

GRINDER
Mahlkonig K30, Mahlkonig Peak, Mahlkonig EK

OPENING HOURS
Mon-Fri
8am-4pm
Sat 10am-10pm
(pizza pop up 5pm-10.30pm)

Gluten FREE

BEANS AVAILABLE INSTORE

ALTERNATIVE MILK

WIFI

CYCLE FRIENDLY

OUTDOOR SEATING

COFFEE COURSES

---

www.execoffeeroasters.co.uk   T: 01392 271549

f Exe Coffee Roasters   🐦 @execoffeeroast   📷 @execoffeeroasters

MAP 78. CALYPSO COFFEE COMPANY

45 Fleet Street, Torquay, Devon, TQ2 5DW

When it comes to beverages that burst with bold creativity, Lucas, Lana and the team at Calypso Coffee never run short of ideas.

Enthusiastic experimentation takes place beneath the handcrafted industrial-chic chandeliers of this spacious cafe on Torquay's Fleet Street.

INSIDER'S TIP CHECK OUT THE REGULAR COFFEE CUPPING SESSIONS

Alongside the classic espresso, filter and cold brew, interesting surprises on the drinks menu include sumptuous lavender and citrus cream coffees, as well as unique homemade tisanes made to closely guarded secret recipes using fruits, spices and seasonings.

Throw in a new range of superfood smoothies, matcha drinks, seriously good New York-style bagels, homemade scones and salted caramel brownies and you can see why this friendly cafe is a magnet for hungry caffeine fiends.

'We're really passionate about what we do and make every single drink with love,' says Lucas, who sees to it that star guests get their moment in the spotlight alongside regular single origin favourites from AllPress.

ESTABLISHED
2015

KEY ROASTER
AllPress Espresso

BREWING METHOD
Espresso, V60, Chemex, AeroPress, cold brew

MACHINE
La Marzocco Linea Classic 3 AV

GRINDER
Mazzer Kony, Super Jolly, Mahlkonig Tanzania

OPENING HOURS
Mon-Sat
8.30am-6pm
Sun 9am-5pm

 Gluten FREE

 BEANS AVAILABLE INSTORE

 ALTERNATIVE MILK

 WIFI

 CYCLE FRIENDLY

 OUTDOOR seating

 FAMILY FRIENDLY

 DISABLED ACCESS

BRING YOUR OWN Cup

T: 01803 213728
f Calypso Coffee Company @calypso_coffee

MAP 79. PORT ESPRESSO

26 Middle Street, Brixham, Devon, TQ5 8ER

The familiar groove of a blues bassline is usually accompanied by the friendly hiss of steaming milk and layers of caffeine-fuelled chatter at Brixham's Port Espresso.

Some customers sit on stools, soaking in the coastal sunshine at the window bar, while the sociable squeeze around the slanting school bench.

INSIDER'S TIP
BRUNCH CENTRES AROUND THE POLESTAR OF LOCALLY-BAKED SOURDOUGH

Whether they've dropped by for a commuter caffeine fix, a get-together brunch or to frequent the badass bakery, there's damn fine coffee for all. Forget laughable lattes, the speciality here is a flat white served with dry humour.

And while the team experiment with new ideas (check out monthly acoustic coffee sessions), the one thing that never changes is the quality of the Voyager coffee, roasted down the road in Buckfastleigh and poured as a double ristretto as standard.

Locals line up for the sausage rolls, pastel de nata and an ever-rotating selection of in-house bakes, all crafted by owner and barista Dan, who also happens to be a retired chef.

ESTABLISHED
2016

KEY ROASTER
Voyager Coffee

BREWING METHOD
Espresso, V60

MACHINE
La Spaziale

GRINDER
Anfim

OPENING HOURS
Mon-Fri
7am-varies
Sat-Sun
8am-varies

---

www.portespresso.co T: 07540 806353

f Port Espresso   @portespresso   @portespresso

MAP№ 80. BAYARDS COVE INN

27 Lower Street, Dartmouth, Devon, TQ6 9AN

A Tudor merchant house turned modern bistro isn't the first place you'd except to find speciality coffee while touring the South West but hey, eclectic finds is what this guide is about.

Steeped in history, Bayards Cove is a one-stop shop in the dashing south Devon town of Dartmouth for pre-dinner pints overlooking the harbour, fully-blown locally sourced suppers or simply a ruddy good cup of coffee and a wedge of cake.

The masterminds behind it all, Charlie and Zuzana Deuchar, took over the 14th century building four years ago, stepping up the jack-of-all-trade inn's coffee offering to speciality standards. Buckfastleigh roaster Voyager provides the beany goods for the bar and also tops up the baristas' coffee knowledge with regular training sessions.

INSIDER'S TIP BRING YOUR KEEPCUP AND EXPLORE DARTMOUTH WITH A SPECIALITY BREW

For road trippers, there's a collection of beautifully refurbished bedrooms above the inn, so it's the perfect pit-stop en route to your next coffee venue and comes with an expertly crafted brew with breakfast in the morning.

ESTABLISHED
2012

KEY ROASTER
Voyager Coffee

BREWING METHOD
Espresso

MACHINE
Sanremo

GRINDER
Sanremo

OPENING HOURS
Mon-Sun
8am-10pm

www.bayardscoveinn.co.uk   T: 01803 839278

f Bayards Cove Inn   🐦 @bayardscoveinn

MAP 81. THE HAIRY BARISTA

69 High Street, Totnes, Devon, TQ9 5PB

After years of planning, husband and wife team Roee 'Hairy Roy' Yekutiel and Ruth Harris finally found the perfect spot for their burgeoning coffee business in the boho town of Totnes.

For those supping in store, seek out the hidden cave seating area and revel in a smooth, nutty house espresso pulled through the customised Conti machine, or opt for one of seven single origins brewed via cafetiere. Beans from London-based Mission are ground on demand as standard.

The eco-conscious pair, who make it their mission to minimise waste and maximise health, stash a mega line-up of brewing accessories, books and KeepCups in store for visitors to buy and take home. Nab one of the reusable glass bottles for your freshly prepared, organic super smoothie and experience an on-the-go wellness kick.

INSIDER'S TIP
ORDER THE VEGAN TURMERIC LATTE FOR AN AROMATIC SIPPING SESH

Accompanying the speciality offering is a small menu of homemade sweet and savoury vegan specialities. Local Boho Cakes stock the counter with an epic array of free-from edibles for sugary satisfaction.

ESTABLISHED
2017

KEY ROASTER
Mission Coffee Works

BREWING METHOD
Espresso, cafetiere

MACHINE
Conti PM custom

GRINDER
Nuova Simonelli Mythos Plus, Mahlkonig

OPENING HOURS
Mon-Fri
8am-5pm
Sat 9am-6pm

Gluten FREE

BEANS AVAILABLE
INSTORE

ALTERNATIVE MILK

WIFI

FAMILY FRIENDLY

DISABLED ACCESS

BRING YOUR OWN CUP

COFFEE COURSES

T: 07916 306723

f The Hairy Barista   🐦 @hairybarista   📷 @the.hairy.barista

MAP № 82. BAYARDS KITCHEN

Shops at Dartington, Shinners Bridge, Totnes, Devon, TQ9 6TQ

When the owners of two successful cafes spend their wedding anniversary doing a kitchen deep-clean, you know you're onto a winner.

Charlie and Zuzana Deuchar clearly have a passion for their businesses; the original Bayards Cove Inn in Dartmouth and its sister venue at The Shops at Dartington.

INSIDER'S TIP PICK UP A BAG OF VOYAGER BEANS FOR YOUR HOME HOPPER

The couple's new coffee house, Bayards Kitchen, spills into the open with tables set among trees and plants. The alfresco terrace is the perfect spot for a well-poured americano with a side of sunshine, while contemporary interiors provide a cosy snug in which to sip warming lattes when the temperature turns.

As well as glorious caffeine, locally-sourced health-focused fodder is served all day, along with homemade cakes designed to make you purr with delight.

'We came to The Shops at Dartington because its strong ethos of supporting local businesses fits with ours,' explains Charlie. *'We buy from suppliers on our doorstep, including Voyager Coffee from Buckfastleigh.'*

ESTABLISHED
2017

KEY ROASTER
Voyager Coffee

BREWING METHOD
Espresso

MACHINE
Sanremo

GRINDER
Sanremo

OPENING HOURS
Mon-Sun
8.30am-5pm

---

www.bayardskitchen.co.uk   T: 01803 862388

f Bayards Kitchen   🐦 @bayardskitchen

MAP 83. THE ALMOND THIEF

Unit 3-4 Shinners Bridge Workshops, Webbers Way, Dartington, Devon, TQ9 6JY

Tucked in an out-of-the-way industrial unit surrounded by lush Devon countryside, the team behind The Almond Thief are fabricators of lust-inducing craft bakes and superb speciality brews.

The unassuming exterior belies the super slick operation beavering away inside, where a band of busy bakers craft a stonking selection of pastries, breads and brunch beauties every morning.

INSIDER'S TIP DROP BY FOR THE BEST PASTEL DE NATA OUTSIDE OF PORTUGAL

Creative kitchen experimentation means that new toothsome treats are always on the cards, including recent additions such as the Almond-made ice cream and wondrous cream-filled cardamom semla buns (#drool).

It's not all about the FOMO-inducing bakes though. A slice of sprouted rye sourdough or a chocolate rye and sea salt cookie isn't complete until paired with an espresso based drink or V60 from the brew bar. House roaster Origin shares shelf space with guests including Workshop, Round Hill, The Barn, Monmouth and Crankhouse.

ESTABLISHED
2015

KEY ROASTER
Origin Coffee Roasters

BREWING METHOD
Espresso, V60

MACHINE
La Marzocco Linea PB

GRINDER
Mythos One, Mahlkonig EK 43

OPENING HOURS
Tue-Fri
8am-3pm
Sat
9am-3pm

ALTERNATIVE MILK

WIFI

CYCLE FRIENDLY

OUTDOOR SEATING

FAMILY FRIENDLY

---

www.thealmondthief.com T: 01803 411290

f The Almond Thief 🐦 @thealmondthief 📷 @thealmondthief

MAP: 84. ROCKETS & RASCALS

7 Parade, The Barbican, Plymouth, Devon, PL1 2JL

Single origin guest coffees, Italian racing bikes and moreish cakes motivate cyclists from across Devon and Cornwall to employ pedal power to hit up this unique coffee shop on Plymouth's Barbican.

Although it's not just bike buffs who have fallen for the caffeinated cycling emporium: it's won the heart of many a local too.

'We do everything we can to avoid becoming your traditional hipster coffee house,' says owner Steve Toze, who asserts that any tattoos, black t-shirts and beards are pure coincidence.

INSIDER'S TIP THE HOME BAKED CARROT CAKE IS DIVINE WITH A FLAT WHITE

A key player in Plymouth's burgeoning speciality scene, Rockets & Rascals has hooked up with city roaster, The Devon Coffee Company, in the creation of its crowd-pleasing espresso, King of the Cobbles. Plus, there's always a tasty single origin waiting in the wings: often the locals' fave, La Bastilla from Nicaragua.

A familiar presence at city events, this winner of a *Plymouth Herald* City and Waterfront Award has stepped up its training recently to deliver an even more fun, friendly and informed coffee experience.

ESTABLISHED
2013

KEY ROASTER
The Devon
Coffee Company

BREWING METHOD
Espresso,
batch brew

MACHINE
Astoria Perla
Lever

GRINDER
Fiorenzato F64
EVO,
Ceado E37S,
Fiorenzato F6,
Compak K3

OPENING HOURS
Mon-Sat
8am-6pm
Sun
9am-5pm

www.rockettrading.co.uk   T: 01752 927555

f Rockets & Rascals   🐦 @rocketsnrascals   📷 @rockettradingco

MAP 85. THE MAD MERCHANT COFFEE HOUSE

37 New Street, The Barbican, Plymouth, Devon, PL1 2NA

The Mad Merchant may be the new kid on the Plymouth coffee block, yet the lively waterfront hangout is already gaining a firm following of brew-guzzling bibliophiles and creatives.

Mum and daughter team – and avid arts lovers – Kay and Bekah are cultivating a cultural hub in the 16th century former merchant's house.

INSIDER'S TIP: POETRY READINGS, GAMES NIGHTS AND AN ALCOHOL LICENSE ARE ALL IN THE PIPELINE

There's already plenty to explore: zip upstairs with a coffee and chunk of homemade cake to find a bookshop complete with vinyl-adorned walls, then spin the needle on the record player, explore the secluded garden and find a space to drop anchor among other like-minded souls.

Inspiration is fired by Extract's Original Espresso, with guest beans from the Bristol roastery rotating every few months.

The Cafe Racer machine has caused quite a stir with fans declaring it the 'best espresso machine in Plymouth' – the Merchant's transparent model is one of only four in the UK.

ESTABLISHED
2017

KEY ROASTER
Extract Coffee Roasters

BREWING METHOD
Espresso

MACHINE
Sanremo Cafe Racer

GRINDER
Mythos One x 2

OPENING HOURS
Mon-Tue
9am-5pm
Thu-Sat
9am-5pm
Sun
10am-4pm

Gluten FREE

ALTERNATIVE MILK

WIFI

CYCLE FRIENDLY

OUTDOOR seating

FAMILY FRIENDLY

T: 01752 214091

f The Mad Merchant Coffee House 🐦 @madmerchantcafe 📷 @themadmerchant_coffeehouse

86. THE HUTONG CAFE

160 Cremyll Street, Plymouth, Devon, PL1 3RB

We do love exploring a new speciality spot. Especially when it's all cosy nooks, flumpy cushions, hulking great sandwiches and truly outstanding coffee.

After forging a caffeine-fuelled friendship with fellow Devonian, Roastworks, Hutong stocks a cracking array of single origins from the indie outfit for its filter system. Though it's the bold and simple Truth blend that has rocketed in popularity, firmly cementing itself as the cafe's staple espresso – the locals just can't get enough of its punchy aroma.

INSIDER'S TIP MAKE THE MOST OF SUNNY DAYS – THE OUTDOOR AREA IS A PRIME PEOPLE-WATCHING SPOT

Keen to bring the community together, the crew host a bill of buzzing events including psychedelic rock and avant garde jazz concerts, as well as stand up comedy gigs. The night time merrymaking is fuelled with pintxos, wine, espresso cocktails and filter drinks.

Food-wise, you haven't had the true Hutong experience until you've tried the (daily sold-out) rosti stack: twice cooked smoked streaky bacon, well-dressed watercress, free-range poached eggs, and the butteriest rosti Plymouth has ever seen.

ESTABLISHED
2017

KEY ROASTER
Roastworks
Coffee Co.

BREWING METHOD
Espresso, filter,
batch brew

MACHINE
Nuova Simonelli
Premier Maxi
custom

GRINDER
Mahlkonig K30
Air

OPENING HOURS
Mon, Wed-Fri
7.30am-5pm
Sat-Sun
8am-5pm

T: 07455 376377

f The Hutong Cafe   🐦 @thehutongcafe   📷 @thehutongcafe

ROASTERS
DEVON

ROASTWORKS
COFFEE CO.
#88

87. COFFEE FACTORY

Unit 3, Samurai Buildings, Seaton Junction, Axminster, Devon, EX13 7PW

Setting up shop in the Devon countryside seven years ago, Justine and Danny Parfitt began their foray into roasting on a small batch model before graduating to a vintage Probat roaster lovingly known as Dorothy.

'Our goal has always been to make coffee easily accessible for both home and business,' explains Danny.

This ambition has resulted in an impressive subscription service which offers a package for every kind of caffeine addict – from smooth, nutty blends for the casual sipper to sensational single origins to please the speciality purist.

ESTABLISHED
2009

ROASTER
MAKE & SIZE
Vintage Probat
UG 22kg

CAFE ONSITE

BEANS AVAILABLE
ONSITE

ONLINE

COFFEE FACTORY IS GOING FULL STEAM AHEAD, SCOOPING NUMEROUS AWARDS

'The Roasters Choice™ subscription has been with us since the beginning and was the first pack to leave the roastery in 2009. It's a solid favourite with our subscribers and features the team's favourite coffees from the cupping table,' adds Danny.

Curious coffee fans can pay the factory a visit to see Dorothy in action, and taste the freshest beans roasted, ground and brewed on site at the brew bar.

www.thecoffeefactory.co.uk   T: 01297 551259
f Coffee Factory   🐦 @coffee_factory   📷 @coffee_factory

MAP 88. ROASTWORKS COFFEE CO.

Unit 7, Blackdown Park, Willand, Devon, EX15 2FS

'**W**e're all about raising the bar and redefining the standard of consumer coffee,' asserts Will Little of Roastworks near Tiverton.

One way the team have been doing that is through the nationwide launch of the Roastworks capsules via Waitrose this year, making them the first speciality roaster to sell Nespresso-compatible capsules in a UK supermarket.

The other has been through the development of their single house blend, The Truth. *'I love a washed Yirgacheffe Grade 1 espresso as much as the next guy,'* says Will, *'but something has been lost in our endless pursuit of clarity, acidity and exotic flavour. I've had many great coffees executed badly because the coffee has been too difficult to dial in successfully or doesn't work with milk.*

'THIS YEAR ROASTWORKS WAS THE FIRST SPECIALITY ROASTER TO SELL NESPRESSO-COMPATIBLE CAPSULES IN A UK SUPERMARKET'

'What's happened to coffee that just tastes great? Sweet, chocolatey and moreish. The Truth is just that. It's a blend of two exceptional, speciality grade Brazilian and Colombian coffees, roasted so that it's sweet, syrupy and works amazingly as a flat white.'

ESTABLISHED
2014

ROASTER
MAKE & SIZE
G.W. Barth
Menado 60kg,
Probat LG12
12kg,
Ferd. Gothot
5 barrel
sample roaster

OPEN
BY APPOINTMENT

BEANS
AVAILABLE
ONLINE

www.roastworks.co.uk T: 01884 829400

f Roastworks Coffee Co. 🐦 @roastworksdevon 📷 @roastworks_coffee_co

89. EXE COFFEE ROASTERS

19 Heavitree Road, Exeter, Devon, EX1 2LD

It's said that the best things are worth waiting for, and taking the time to craft something spectacular is the ethos that former UKBC semi-finalist Steve Pearson subscribes to at his roastery in Devon.

Roasting from its base in Exeter for the past two years, EXE Coffee Roasters not only harbours a Probat Probatone in the basement, but also a street level coffee shop. The open-style roastery – a swift seven minute dash from the High Street – means visitors can enjoy a brew while taking in the roasting experience in real time.

Steve and his right-hand-roaster Ollie are currently crafting house espresso blend, Neighbourhood, and two single origins which can be sampled upstairs. The duo also offer free training to XCR's wholesale customers and popular Be a Barista courses, which have been running for almost five years.

ESTABLISHED
2014

ROASTER
MAKE & SIZE
Probat
Probatone
12kg

CAFE
ONSITE

OPEN
TO THE PUBLIC

COFFEE
COURSES

BEANS
AVAILABLE
ONSITE

'THE OPEN-STYLE ROASTERY MEANS VISITORS CAN ENJOY A BREW WHILE TAKING IN THE ROASTING EXPERIENCE IN REAL TIME'

'It's a total hands-on process,' explains Steve. 'From the hand branding of each bag to delivering products to our customers (sometimes by bike), we're proud that we roast every bean we supply.'

www.execoffeeroasters.co.uk   T: 01392 271549

Exe Coffee Roasters   @execoffeeroast   @execoffeeroasters

DON'T BE BLAND

Working with the best food, drink, hospitality and tourism businesses.
Call us to add a pinch of salt to your
branding, design, copywriting and magazines

salt media

www.saltmedia.co.uk | 01271 859299 | ideas@saltmedia.co.uk | f 𝕏 ⓞ
Publishers of food Magazine, The Independent Coffee Guides and The Trencherman's Guide

90. CRANKHOUSE COFFEE

Great Matridge, Longdown, Exeter, Devon, EX6 7BE

It's amazing how far Crankhouse has come since it started applying heat to bean in 2014. Nowadays, it's a household name for coffee lovers in the South West, who give the nod of approval when spotting the beans in cafes up and down this corner of the country.

Owner and alchemist Dave Stanton has probably nabbed the most picturesque spot in Devon to house his roastery and coffee school. In countryside on the edge of Dartmoor, he can escape the hustle and bustle of city life and get back to simple pleasures, like the magic of turning beans into a complex and full-bodied brew.

Within the converted barn, Dave selects green beans with exciting and diverse characteristics and roasts them in a way to preserve and enhance their flavour. *'I work with an Italian 1995 Petroncini TT7.5, my senses and a little science,'* he says.

ESTABLISHED
2014

ROASTER
MAKE & SIZE
Petroncini TT7.5

DAVE DOCUMENTS HIS COFFEE MUSINGS AND MORNING TASTINGS ON HIS FACEBOOK PAGE, WHICH IS WELL WORTH A LIKE

Look out for Crankhouse in speciality establishments across the South West and further afield – sometimes you'll even find a bespoke blend creation. Even better, book on to one of Dave's coffee courses, regular cuppings or roastery tours for the full Crankhouse experience.

www.crankhousecoffee.co.uk   T: 07588 020288

f Crankhouse Coffee   🐦 @crankhouseroast   📷 @crankhouseroast

MAP 91. VOYAGER COFFEE

Unit 6, Mardle Way Business Park, Buckfastleigh, Devon, TQ11 0JL

One knock out cappuccino in Italy – expertly prepared by a seasoned barista using fabulous coffee – was all it took for Andrew Tucker to realise that he could do the same in the South West.

After successfully supplying market leading Sanremo machines, speciality coffee and barista training, in 2013 Coffee West took the next step and bought the first South African Genio 30kg roaster. The one-of-a-kind machine formed the backbone of Voyager Coffee and is still used to roast its selection of single origin and micro lot coffees alongside a shiny new Genio 15kg.

COFFEE COURSES COVER EVERYTHING FROM BARISTA BASICS TO LATTE ART AND TRAIN THE TRAINER

The roastery on the edge of Dartmoor is a hive of activity: 'The doors to our roastery and training academy are always open for the caffeine curious to discover the art of coffee cupping and learn how to extract the fantastic flavours with our state of the art equipment,' says Andrew.

The team still retain their specialism in Sanremo machines, Curtis brewing equipment and are leaders in technical support, with engineers across the region.

ESTABLISHED
2001

ROASTER
MAKE & SIZE
Genio 30kg,
Genio 15kg

OPEN
BY APPOINTMENT

COFFEE
COURSES

BEANS
AVAILABLE

ONSITE

ONLINE

www.voyagercoffee.co.uk   T: 01364 644440

f Voyager Coffee Roasters   🐦 @voyagercoffee   📷 @voyagercoffee

92. THE DEVON COFFEE COMPANY

Unit 195 Faraday Mill, Oakfield Terrace Road, Plymouth, Devon, PL4 0ST

Upping sticks and moving to a spanking new roastery in 2016, The Devon Coffee Company is all about customer-tailored experiences designed to plunge both coffee connoisseurs and filter freshers into the world of speciality.

Within the 2,000 square foot facility we've built a roastery, training room and warehouse where we can now offer tasting sessions and barista training,' explains owner Andrew Baker.

For trade customers looking for creative involvement, a new bespoke service offers full control over each order, from choice of green beans through to adjustments in the roast profile.

THE TEAM HAVE DEVELOPED THREE NEW SEASONAL ESPRESSO BLENDS, EACH WITH A DISTINCT FLAVOUR PROFILE

Domestic dabblers are equally well catered for by The Devon Coffee Club which delivers a range of subscription coffees prepared for the full spectrum of brewing methods.

And the aim of the game? *'To offer a tailored experience to our customers, while providing guidance and support through the ever-evolving world of speciality coffee,'* smiles Andrew.

ESTABLISHED
2011

ROASTER
MAKE & SIZE
BESCA 15kg,
North 1kg

OPEN
BY APPOINTMENT

COFFEE
COURSES

BEANS
AVAILABLE

ONLINE

www.devoncoffeecompany.com   T: 01752 222567

The Devon Coffee Company   @devoncoffeeco   @devoncoffeecompany

STRONG
ATLANTIC HIGHWAY
ADOLFOS

STRONG
ADOLFOS
#95

CORNWALL

*All locations are approximate

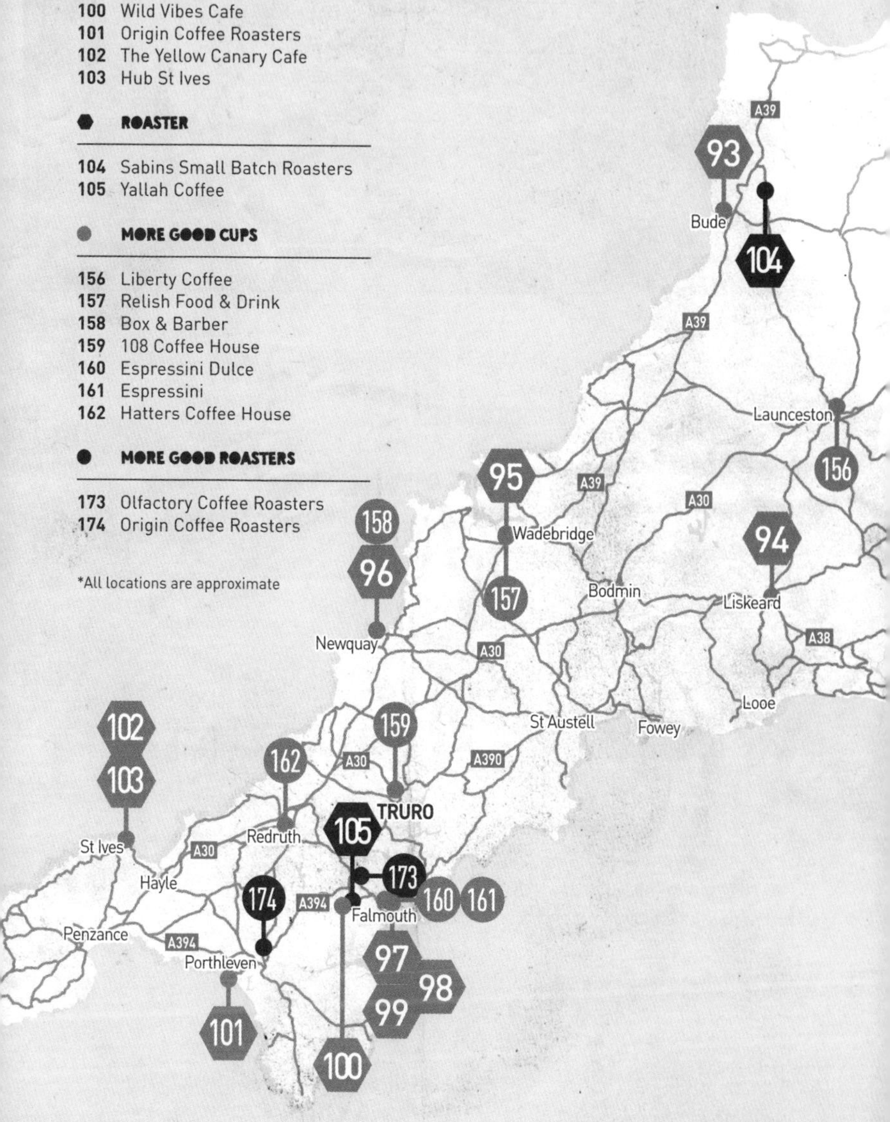

A39

93

Bude

104

A39

Launceston

95

A39

158

A30

156

96

Wadebridge

94

157

Bodmin

Liskeard

Newquay

A30

A38

102

159

St Austell   Fowey

Looe

103

162

A30

A390

105   TRURO

St Ives

A30

173

Redruth

Hayle

174

A394

160   161

Penzance

A394

Falmouth

101

Porthleven

97

100

98

99

MAP № 93. NORTH COAST WINE CO

1 Lansdown Road, Bude, Cornwall, EX23 8BH

North Coast Wine Co isn't your standard offie – or coffee shop for that matter. The independent wine merchant is more an emporium of 500 beverages which you can quaff in-store or guzzle later at home.

If you're drinking in, once you've worked your way through the creative cocktail list, you'll want to hit the brew menu for a sobering caffeine hit.

Park yourself in a 1930s cinema seat and sip an espresso while you peruse the array of goodies for sale from Cornwall and further afield. Coffee beans, hand roasted at micro roastery Monsoon Estates, can also be added to your basket.

INSIDER'S TIP TRY OUT THE EIGHT BOTTLE ENOMATIC WINE TASTING MACHINE

'Our carefully selected roast and simple approach to crafting coffee is what makes North Coast Wine Co a perfect place for a brew,' says owner Oliver Tullett, who has developed the business from an outdated off-licence into a delightful drinking and dining destination.

Whether you need the low-down on the best vintages, tips on how to make the perfect shot or brewing techniques for crafting delicious coffee at home, a team of experts is always on hand to advise.

ESTABLISHED
2015

KEY ROASTER
Monsoon Estates

BREWING METHOD
Espresso

MACHINE
La Spaziale S5

GRINDER
Mahlkonig K30

OPENING HOURS
Mon-Thu
10am-6pm
Fri-Sat
10am-9pm

www.ncwine.co.uk T: 01288 354304
f North Coast Wine Co LTD 🐦 @ncwine1 📷 @northcoastwineco

MAP № 94. OLIVE & CO.

Windsor Place, Liskeard, Cornwall, PL14 4BH

Naming their coffee shop after their daughter, owners Roxy and Lee may be the 'Co.' at this cosy spot, but it looks like little Olive is the real boss.

This family-run business does a roaring trade in the heart of the pretty market town of Liskeard thanks to a constant stream of Monmouth coffee and delish homemade pastries and cakes.

Expect a double shot as standard, with milk from nearby Trewithen Dairy and accompanying bakes that change daily – make sure you're first in the queue for the choccie coffee cardamom cake, as it goes quickly.

INSIDER'S TIP: THERE'S A SECRET GARDEN … KEEP IT TO YOURSELF

Eclectic decor and local art make this a charming oasis in which to enjoy the ever-changing pageant of local guest roasts from the likes of Origin, Sabins and Voyager. It's also one of the best places in the area for a brilliant brekkie. Vegetarians and vegans can find plenty of gratifying goodies too, including an excellent signature handcrafted veggie burger.

Take note: you're entering a wifi-free zone, a feature that encourages a sociable buzz at this friendly hideout.

ESTABLISHED
2016

KEY ROASTER
Monmouth
Coffee Company

BREWING METHOD
Espresso,
cold brew

MACHINE
La Spaziale

GRINDER
Mazzer

OPENING HOURS
Mon-Sat
8.45am-4pm

Gluten FREE

BEANS AVAILABLE INSTORE

ALTERNATIVE MILK

OUTDOOR seating

FAMILY FRIENDLY

BRING YOUR OWN cup

---

www.olivecocafe.com T: 07968 420015

f Olive & Co. 🐦 @olivecocafe 📷 @olivecocafe

95. STRONG ADOLFOS

Hawksfield, A39, Wadebridge, Cornwall, PL27 7LR

When Mathilda and John began constructing a Swedish-Cornish-biker-surfer cafe at an out-of-town road stop, whispers swept over the community. *'They won't last long out there,'* people prophesied. But three years later, Strong Adolfos is absolutely thriving.

The success is due to a number of factors. Firstly, the team use Cornish roaster heavyweight, Origin, to create a quality coffee – which is pimped with epic latte art.

INSIDER'S TIP EXPLORE THE NEIGHBOURING DELI AND FURNITURE RECLAMATION STORE FOR MORE CREATIVE INSPO

Then there are the banging breakfasts (think homemade baked beans and thick cut bacon with sourdough) and lunches, including great veggie options, which are all created with local produce by talented head chef Donna Ashton.

But the ultimate reason why regulars can't stay away from this Atlantic Highway pit-stop is the cake. Inspired by Mathilda's Swedish ritual of fika, you'll find Scandinavian delights such as chocolate kladdkaka, cardamom buns and light-as-a-cloud drömmar (dream) cookies.

ESTABLISHED
2013

KEY ROASTER
Origin Coffee Roasters

BREWING METHOD
Espresso, filter

MACHINE
La Marzocco Linea PB

GRINDER
Nuova Simonelli Mythos One

OPENING HOURS
Mon-Fri
8.30am-4pm
Sat-Sun
9am-4pm

---

www.strongadolfos.com   T: 01208 816949

f Strong Adolfo's   @strongadolfos   @strongadolfos

MAP № 96. FIN & CO.

Above Watershed, 3-5 Bank Street, Newquay, Cornwall, TR7 1EP

I n a town dominated by major surf brands, it was a plucky move for Jake Patterson and James Wright to launch their indie board shop, Watershed, right in the middle of it all.

The risk paid off and as a result of the venture's success, five years on the duo have just embarked on their next big project: opening a speciality coffee shop (complete with a sneaky suntrap seating area) upstairs.

The design-led approach that defines the brand shines through in the cafe too, and it's a space in which to hang out with friends or even get a bit of creative inspo with colleagues.

INSIDER'S TIP LIVE VICARIOUSLY THROUGH THE ONLINE JOURNAL OF SURF TRIPS AND LATEST PROJECTS

Working with Cornish roaster Yallah to develop a signature Fin & Co. blend, the silky espresso pulled through the Victoria Arduino machine is also available to pick up at any of the Watershed stores. And those in favour of fruitier flavours are well served by the Adventure blend with notes of jasmine, bergamot and papaya.

ESTABLISHED
2017

KEY ROASTER
Yallah Coffee

BREWING METHOD
Espresso

MACHINE
Victoria Arduino

GRINDER
Victoria Arduino

OPENING HOURS
Mon-Sun
9am-5.30pm

www.watershedbrand.com T: 01637 498121

f Watershed 🐦 @watershedshop 📷 @finandconqy

THE FONDEST
memories MADE
ARE
WHEN gathered
~AROUND~
THE TABLE

HUB ST IVES
#103

ᴹᴬᴾ 97. GOOD VIBES CAFE

28 Killigrew Street, Falmouth, Cornwall, TR11 3PN

Since Dan Rossiter took over this Cornish coffee shop in June 2016, he has artfully built on its reputation for knocking out beautiful pours and plated creations.

Good Vibes focuses on offering the people of Falmouth carefully crafted coffee and generous portions of outstanding food which you don't need to re-mortgage the house to experience.

Hailing from Birmingham, but proudly championing the best of Cornwall's produce, Dan teamed up with Origin to provide the beans and says, *'For me, it's about collaborating with interesting businesses with an ethical approach which also stray away from the norm'.*

INSIDER'S TIP FOUR-LEGGED FRIENDS ARE ALSO INVITED FOR EARLY MORNING BREWS AND AFTERNOON FLATTIES

Community spirit shines through here and local artists' work jostles for attention with posters promoting vibrant parties, festivals and clubs as you sit 'n' sip.

Keep an eye on Good Vibes' Facebook page for food porn, updates and details of upcoming events, especially the brilliant vegan tasting evenings.

ESTABLISHED
2013

KEY ROASTER
Origin Coffee Roasters

BREWING METHOD
Espresso, batch brew

MACHINE
La Marzocco

GRINDER
Nuova Simonelli Mythos One

OPENING HOURS
Mon-Sat
8.30am-5pm
Sun 10am-2pm

Gluten FREE

ALTE RNA TIVE MILK

WIFI

T: 01326 211870

 Good Vibes Cafe   @goodvibescafefalmouth

MAP 98. PICNIC CORNWALL

14 Church Street, Falmouth, Cornwall, TR11 3DR

Whether you're after a quick coffee to-go or have time to stop and savour each sip, a quality Origin espresso is always guaranteed at this award winning indie coffee shop.

Seasonal blends roasted in Helston are paired with local milk from Trewithen Dairy, making Picnic a popular spot for those seeking a brew that's crafted in the county.

The boutique of bounty (it also has a deli and hamper service) is like entering a walk-in larder stocked with the most delicious Cornish goodies such as Tregothnan tea, gin, wines, chocolates, cheeses and charcuterie.

INSIDER'S TIP FILL A PICNIC HAMPER, GRAB A COFFEE TO-GO AND YOU'RE SET FOR AN ALFRESCO CORNISH FEAST

And if the aroma of freshly baked cakes and patisserie doesn't tempt you to linger, the sandwiches, organic pasties and sausage rolls – made with free-range pork, apricot and rosemary – will probably do the trick.

Brekkies of porridge, muesli, granola and yogurt accompany coffee for a healthy morning high, or ditch the good intentions in favour of sarnies stacked with bacon, sausage and tomato relish.

ESTABLISHED
2013

KEY ROASTER
Origin Coffee
Roasters

BREWING METHOD
Espresso

MACHINE
La Marzocco
FB80

GRINDER
Mazzer Luigi

OPENING HOURS
Mon-Sat
9am-5pm
Sun
10am-5pm
(extended in
summer)

---

www.picniccornwall.co.uk   T: 01326 211655

f Picnic Cornwall   🐦 @picniccornwall   📷 @picnic_cornwall

MAP № 99. GYLLY BEACH CAFE

Cliff Road, Falmouth, Cornwall, TR11 4PA

As spectacular seaside settings go, it doesn't get much better than Gylly Beach Cafe. This coastal favourite sits smack bang on silver sands amid circling seagulls and crashing waves.

Grab an Origin Resolute espresso and see if you can manoeuvre your rear into one of the popular terrace seats offering dazzling views across the waves to the Lizard Peninsula and Helford River.

INSIDER'S TIP: CARPE CRUSTULAM (SEIZE THE CAKE)! BROWNIES, CAKES AND MUFFINS CHANGE DAILY

Whatever time of day you visit, the ever-changing seascapes, and seasonal seafood from *MasterChef The Professionals* quarter-finalist Dale McIntosh make this award winning cafe, with its own bakery, ideal for beach-side banqueting.

In the morning, linger over a Cornish flat white and a brekkie bursting with omega goodness such as vanilla and coconut chia seed pudding with chargrilled peaches. At lunchtime, tuck into imaginative plates such as roasted mackerel or the squid burger. While in the evening, watch them fire up the outdoor grill for a flaming feast of fresh local fish and a decaf San Fermin americano.

ESTABLISHED
2000

KEY ROASTER
Origin Coffee Roasters

BREWING METHOD
Espresso

MACHINE
La Marzocco

GRINDER
Expresso Italiano

OPENING HOURS
Mon-Sat
9am-late

www.gyllybeach.com T: 01326 312884
f Gylly Beach Cafe 🐦 @gyllybeachcafe 📷 @gyllybeachcafe

MAP 100. WILD VIBES CAFE

Argal and College Water Park, Mabe Burnthouse, Penryn, Cornwall, TR10 9JF

It can be a drag having to choose between eye-popping panoramas and somewhere serving a half decent cup of coffee, but thankfully there's no compromise at Wild Vibes on the edge of Argal Lake.

Teaming up with Fitness Wild, Dan Rossiter launched Wild Vibes in May 2017 after carving out a reputation for pulling cracking Origin coffee at his Good Vibes hangout in Falmouth.

We'd recommend getting the crew together for a day at the lake – making sure everyone packs a hearty appetite.

INSIDER'S TIP JOIN THE PERSONAL TRAINING GROUP 'FITNESS WILD' WHICH RUNS REGULAR SESSIONS HERE

Start with a 2km walk through picturesque woodland, wetland and meadow then, come lunchtime, take your pick from Wild Vibes' locally sourced menu which is big on bold vegan options and seasonal compilations.

Round off your trip with a generous slice of homemade cake and a cup of Origin's Resolute blend via espresso, while you take in the reflection of the sun, sky and birds on the mirror-flat lake. It's a feast for the eyes *and* the palate.

ESTABLISHED
2017

KEY ROASTER
Origin Coffee Roasters

BREWING METHOD
Espresso, batch brew

MACHINE
La Marzocco

GRINDER
Nuova Simonelli Mythos One

OPENING HOURS
Mon-Sat
9am-4pm
Sun 10am-4pm

T: 01326 702105
f Wild Vibes @wildvibesargal

MAP 101. ORIGIN COFFEE ROASTERS

Harbour Head, Porthleven, Cornwall, TR13 9JY

S lap bang in the centre of Porthleven's pretty horseshoe harbour, amid a cluster of restaurants and stores, Origin's cosy coffee shop is a port in a storm on a blustery day and delightful suntrap with outdoor seating when it's fine.

Wave riders from across the UK – drawn to the hollow green barrels of the Porthleven swell – fuel their watery fun at this popular coffee shop at the heart of the village community.

INSIDER'S TIP ENJOY A COOL GLASS OF NITRO COLD BREW AVAILABLE ON TAP

As you would expect at an Origin outlet, talented coffee chemists create a mean speciality cup which includes freshly-roasted single origin espresso, filter coffees and Sandows nitro cold brew on tap.

Beans cooked up on two Loring Smart roasters at Origin's Helston headquarters down the road are crafted into outstanding cups by committed baristas whose raison d'etre is to welcome, educate and help customers enjoy the best cup of coffee.

The whole team share a passion to pass on their love of brewing and speciality coffee, and enjoy imparting the knowledge and tools to help others confidently craft a cup at home.

ESTABLISHED
2013

KEY ROASTER
Origin Coffee Roasters

BREWING METHOD
Espresso, pourover, batch brew filter

MACHINE
La Marzocco Strada ABR

GRINDER
Nuova Simonelli Mythos One

OPENING HOURS
Mon-Sun
9am-5pm
(Mar-Oct)

www.origincoffee.co.uk   T: 01326 574337
f Origin Coffee Roasters   🐦 @origincoffee   📷 @origincoffeeroasters

MAP № 102. THE YELLOW CANARY CAFE

12 Fore Street, St Ives, Cornwall, TR26 1AB

A vibrant yellow sign swinging in the breeze indicates where to stop for speciality coffee on St Ives' cobbled Fore Street.

If you're in a rush, grab your Origin-roasted house or seasonal espresso from the Yellow Canary hatch – with a freshly baked pastel de nata oozing with creamy custard if it's that kinda day.

INSIDER'S TIP IF YOU'RE A REGULAR, ASK ABOUT THE LOYALTY SCHEME AND GET MORE BEANS FOR YOUR BUCK

If you've time to stick around, grab a spot inside this cosy cafe at the centre of town to savour a flat white – made with unhomogenised milk from Trink Dairy just down the road – while deciding which of the luscious bakes to try first. Owners Paul and Ylena Haase rise early to get slabs of deliciousness (try the maple syrup and butter laden flapjacks) into the oven and out onto the counter for the hungry hordes.

With a 45 year history in the town, the family-run cafe remains as popular for its whopping sarnies, award winning pasties and sumptuous cream teas as it is for top-notch speciality brews.

ESTABLISHED
1972

KEY ROASTER
Origin Coffee Roasters

BREWING METHOD
Espresso, AeroPress

MACHINE
La Marzocco Linea PB

GRINDER
Mazzer Major E

OPENING HOURS
Mon-Sun
Summer
7am-10pm
Winter
9am-5pm
(Mar-Nov)

T: 01736 797118

f The Yellow Canary Cafe 🐦 @yellowcanarycaf @theyellowcanarycafe

№103. HUB ST IVES

4 The Wharf, St Ives, Cornwall, TR26 1LF

The original hangout in St Ives for 'burgers, dogs, beers and damn good coffee', this all-day feasting fiesta has been a firm favourite with resident brew swiggers and Cornwall day-trippers since 2003.

As well as being experts in cracking ice-cold craft beers and blending ice cream shakes, the guys at Hub have been trained by the team at Origin to craft first class coffee using the Cornish roaster's Pathfinder blend.

INSIDER'S TIP RETURN MID-AFTERNOON FOR AN AMERICANO AND A WEDGE OF CAKE

With blackberry and redcurrant notes and an indulgently jammy body with a long, sweet finish, the house roast works as well in espresso drinks as it does lavished with steamed milk in a signature flat white.

Friendly vibes, a roomy balcony and views over the harbour make the wait between a morning brew and the acceptable hour at which to dig into the stacked patties, dirty dogs and pimped mac 'n' cheese a little easier to bear.

ESTABLISHED
2003

KEY ROASTER
Origin Coffee Roasters

BREWING METHOD
Espresso

MACHINE
La Marzocco Strada custom

GRINDER
Nuova Simonelli Mythos One

OPENING HOURS
Mon-Sun
9am-10pm

ALTERNATIVE MILK

WIFI

CYCLE FRIENDLY

OUTDOOR SEATING

FAMILY FRIENDLY

DISABLED ACCESS

www.hub-stives.co.uk   T: 01736 799099

f Hub   🐦 @hubstives   📷 @hubstives

CORNWALL ROASTERS

Butterfly Barn, Hersham, Bude, Cornwall, EX23 9LZ

Success hasn't gone to Emma and Paul Sabin's heads. They may have collected quite the cult following for their boutique Bude brand, but the award-shunning couple are sticking firmly to their roots.

'In our third year of roasting, we've felt real direction in remaining a small batch roaster,' says Emma.

Even with growth in the business – you'll find the addition of a second Toper at the secluded Cornish smallholding this year – the family outfit are more about bettering the world than bringing in the big bucks.

Always on the lookout for new ventures and opportunities, the pair have supported upcoming producers by sourcing from an emerging young coffee entrepreneur in Myanmar whose beans scored an impressive SCA 87.16 in the National Cupping Competition.

'WE'VE SOURCED A SECOND ROASTER WHICH SITS WITHIN OUR SMALLHOLDING. WE'RE VERY MUCH A FAMILY BUSINESS'

And it's not just people they're benefitting, either. Pushing forward with a conservation coffee, they're helping secure the future of an endangered bat species.

ESTABLISHED
2014

ROASTER
MAKE & SIZE
Toper x 2

OPEN
BY APPOINTMENT

COFFEE
COURSES

BEANS
AVAILABLE

ONSITE

ONLINE

www.sabinscoffee.co.uk T: 01288 321660

f Sabins Coffee 🐦 @sabinscoffee 📷 @sabins_coffee

ORIGIN
COFFEE
ROASTERS
#101

105. YALLAH COFFEE

Argal Home Farm, Kergilliack, Falmouth, Cornwall, TR11 5PD

At Yallah Coffee, beans roasted in a barn in the middle of Cornwall's rural wilds are crafted to appeal to everyday adventurers.

'We set out to build an honest business with a low environmental impact that returned something to source,' explains founder Richard Blake.

'Obviously we always want the coffee to speak the loudest, but we're all passionate about growing a good company too. At the moment we use compostable packaging and eco-friendly couriers, while the chaff from roasting is used to partially fuel the farm's biomass boiler.'

ESTABLISHED
2014

ROASTER
MAKE & SIZE
Otto Swadlo 3kg,
Virey Garnier
15kg

OPEN
TO THE PUBLIC

COFFEE COURSES

BEANS AVAILABLE

ONSITE

ONLINE

THE NEW HOUSE COFFEE HAS BEEN CREATED FROM A DIRECT TRADE PARTNERSHIP WITH EIGHT PRODUCERS IN NICARAGUA

Most of Yallah's coffee is traded directly, working with small groups of producers in Brazil and Nicaragua to source its House Coffee.

Inspiration for its popular Trust range comes from the likes of *'early wake-up calls, sheltering from the rain and a comforting boost when you need it'*. The Explore range, meanwhile, is *'all about making people stop and think - and ask for another cup of coffee'*.

www.yallahcoffee.co.uk   T: 01326 727383

f Yallah Coffee Roasters   🐦 @yallahcoffee   📷 @yallahcoffee

MORE GOOD CUPS

SO MANY EXCEPTIONAL PLACES TO DRINK COFFEE ...

MAP Nº 106
WRIGHTS FOOD EMPORIUM
Golden Grove Arms, Llanarthne,
Carmarthenshire, SA32 8JU

www.wrightsfood.co.uk

MAP Nº 107
WATERLOO TEA – LAKESIDE
17-19 Clearwater Way, Lakeside, Cardiff,
CF23 6DL

www.waterlootea.com

MAP Nº 108
WATERLOO TEA – PENYLAN
5 Waterloo Gardens, Penylan, Cardiff,
CF23 5AA

www.waterlootea.com

MAP Nº 109
THE EARLY BIRD
38 Woodville Road, Cardiff, CF24 4EB

www.earlybirdbakery.co.uk

MAP Nº 110
KIN+ILK – PONTCANNA
31 Cathedral Road, Pontcanna, Cardiff,
CF11 9HB

www.kinandilk.com

MAP Nº 111
HARD LINES – CENTRAL MARKET
Unit 25, Cardiff Central Market,
St Mary Street, Cardiff, CF10 1AU.

MAP Nº 112
KIN+ILK – CAPITAL QUARTER
Capital Quarter 1, Smart Way,
Tyndall Street, Cardiff, CF10 4BZ

www.kinandilk.com

MAP Nº 113
WATERLOO TEA – PENARTH
Washington Buildings, 1-3 Stanwell Road,
Penarth, Glamorgan, CF64 2AD

www.waterlootea.com

114
NEW ENGLAND COFFEE HOUSE
1 Digbeth Street, Stow-on-the-Wold,
Gloucestershire, GL54 1BN

www.newenglandcoffeehouse.co.uk

115
COTSWOLD ARTISAN COFFEE
5 Bishop's Walk, Cricklade Street,
Cirencester, Gloucestershire, GL7 1JH

116
CHANDOS DELI – BRISTOL
79 Henleaze Road, Bristol, BS9 4JP

www.chandosdeli.com

117
TRADEWIND ESPRESSO
118 Whiteladies Road, Clifton,
Bristol, BS8 2RP

www.tradewindespresso.com

118
BRISTOL COFFEE HOUSE
121 Whiteladies Road, Clifton,
Bristol, BS8 2PL

www.bristolcoffeehouse.co.uk

119
MOCKINGBIRD
58 Alma Vale Road, Clifton,
Bristol, BS8 2HS

www.mockingbirdcafe.tumblr.com

120
SPICER+COLE – CLIFTON
9 Princess Victoria Street, Clifton Village,
Bristol, BS8 4BX

www.spicerandcole.co.uk

121
CAFE RONAK
169 Gloucester Road, Bristol, BS7 8BE

www.caferonak.co.uk

122
SPICER+COLE – GLOUCESTER ROAD
16 The Promenade, Gloucester Road,
Bristol, BS7 8AE

www.spicerandcole.co.uk

123
THE BRISTOLIAN CAFE
2 Picton Street, Montpelier, Bristol, BS6 5QA

www.thebristolian.co.uk

124
PINKMANS
85 Park Street, Bristol, BS1 5PJ

www.pinkmans.co.uk

125
FRISKA – PARK STREET
87 Park Street, Clifton, Bristol, BS1 5PJ

www.friskafood.com

126
BEATROOT CAFE
20-21 Lower Park Row, Bristol, BS1 5BN

www.beatrootcafe.com

127
BLUE PIG CAFE
33 Colston Avenue, Bristol, BS1 4UA

www.bluepigcafe.co.uk

128
FULL COURT PRESS
59 Broad Street, Bristol, BS1 2EJ

www.fcpcoffee.com

129
FRISKA – VICTORIA STREET
36 Victoria Street, Bristol, BS1 6BY

www.friskafood.com

130
NO12 EASTON
12 High Street, Easton, Bristol, BS5 6DL

www.12easton.com

131
ESTE KITCHEN
7 Greenbank Road, Easton, Bristol, BS5 6EZ

www.estekitchen.com

132
BOSTON TEA PARTY – BATH ALFRED STREET
8 Alfred Street, Bath, BA1 2QU

www.bostonteaparty.co.uk

133
CHANDOS DELI – BATH
12 George Street, Bath, BA1 2EH

www.chandosdeli.com

134
HUNTER & SONS
14-15 Milsom Place, Bath, BA1 1BZ

www.hunter-sons.co.uk

135
THE GREEN ROCKET
1 Pierrepont Street, Bath, BA1 1LB

www.thegreenrocket.co.uk

136
THE FORUM COFFEE HOUSE
3-5 Forum Buildings, St James's Parade, Bath, BA1 1UG

www.bathforum.co.uk

137
COFFEE LAB UK
35 Blue Boar Row, Salisbury, Wiltshire, SP1 1DA

www.coffeelabuk.com

138
BOSTON TEA PARTY – SALISBURY
Old George Inn, 13 High Street, Salisbury, Wiltshire, SP1 2NJ

www.bostonteaparty.co.uk

139
BOSCANOVA
650 Christchurch Road, Bournemouth, Dorset, BH1 4BP

www.thecaffeinehustler.com

140
SOUTH COAST ROAST
24 Richmond Hill, Bournemouth, Dorset, BH2 6EJ

www.thecaffeinehustler.com

141
THE DANCING GOAT
31 Parr Street, Poole, Dorset, BH14 0JX

www.thedancinggoat.co.uk

MAP 142
FINCA – POUNDBURY
The Buttercross, The Buttermarket, Poundbury, Dorchester, Dorset, DT1 3AZ

www.fincacoffee.co.uk

MAP 143
BOSTON TEA PARTY – HONITON
Monkton House, 53 High Street, Honiton, Devon, EX14 1PW

www.bostonteaparty.co.uk

MAP 144
IVAN'S COFFEE
The Bike Shop, 30 Leat Street, Tiverton, Devon, EX16 5LG

MAP 145
BLOCK
12-14 Butchers Row, Barnstaple, Devon, EX31 1BW

www.eatatblock.com

MAP 146
BIKE SHED CAFE
The Square, Barnstaple, Devon, EX32 8LS

www.bikesheduk.com

MAP 147
CREDITON COFFEE COMPANY
1 Market Square House, Market Street, Crediton, Devon, EX17 2BN

www.creditoncoffeee.co.uk

MAP 148
ARTIGIANO
248 High Street, Exeter, Devon, EX4 3PZ

www.artigiano.uk.com

MAP 149
CHANDOS DELI – EXETER
1 Roman Walk, Princesshay, Exeter, Devon, EX1 1GN

www.chandosdeli.com

MAP 150
DEVON COFFEE
88 Queen Street, Exeter, Devon, EX4 3RP

www.devoncoffee.co.uk

MAP 151
THE GLORIOUS ART HOUSE
120 Fore Street, Exeter, Devon, EX4 3JQ

www.theglorious.co.uk

MAP 152
CAFE AT 36
36 Cowick Street, Exeter, Devon, EX4 1AW

www.cafeat36.co.uk

MAP 153
COASTERS COFFEE COMPANY
Unit 1, Abbots Quay, Prince of Wales Road, Kingsbridge, Devon, TQ7 1DY

MAP 154
JACKA BAKERY
38 Southside Street, The Barbican, Plymouth, Devon, PL1 2LE

MAP 155
BOSTON TEA PARTY – PLYMOUTH
Jamaica House, 82-84 Vauxhall Street, Sutton Harbour, Plymouth, Devon, PL4 0EX

www.bostonteaparty.co.uk

MAP N° 156
LIBERTY COFFEE
4 Northgate Street, Launceston,
Cornwall, PL15 8BD

www.liberty-coffee.co.uk

MAP N° 157
RELISH FOOD & DRINK
Foundry Court, Wadebridge,
Cornwall, PL27 7QN

www.relishcornwall.co.uk

MAP N° 158
BOX & BARBER
82 Fore Street, Newquay, Cornwall, TR7 1EY

MAP N° 159
108 COFFEE HOUSE
108c Kenway Street, Truro,
Cornwall, TR1 3DJ

www.108coffee.co.uk

MAP N° 160
ESPRESSINI DULCE
45 Arwenack Street, Falmouth,
Cornwall, TR11 3JH

www.espressini.co.uk

MAP N° 161
ESPRESSINI
39 Killigrew Street, Falmouth,
Cornwall, TR11 3PW

www.espressini.co.uk

MAP N° 162
HATTERS COFFEE HOUSE
21 Fore Street, Redruth, Cornwall, TR15 2BD

PICNIC
CORNWALL #98

MORE GOOD ROASTERS

ADDITIONAL HOT HAULS FOR YOUR HOPPER

MAP.Nº 163
FOOTPRINT COFFEE
Ednol Farm, Kinnerton, Presteigne, Powys, LD8 2PF

www.footprintcoffee.co.uk

MAP.Nº 164
JAMES GOURMET COFFEE CO
Chase Industrial Estate, Alton Road, Ross-on-Wye, Herefordshire, HR9 5WA

www.jamesgourmetcoffee.com

MAP.Nº 165
LUFKIN COFFEE ROASTERS
183a Kings Road, Cardiff, CF11 9DF

www.lufkincoffee.com

MAP.Nº 166
QUANTUM COFFEE ROASTERS
58 Bute Street, Quayside, Cardiff, CF10 5BN

www.quantumcoffeeroasters.co.uk

MAP.Nº 167
RAVE COFFEE
Unit 7, Stirling Works, Love Lane, Cirencester, Gloucestershire, GL7 1YG

www.ravecoffee.co.uk

MAP.Nº 168
TRIPLE CO ROAST
123 Stokes Croft, Bristol, BS1 3RZ

www.triplecoroast.com

MAP.Nº 169
TWO DAY COFFEE ROASTERS
135 St Michael's Hill, Bristol, BS2 8BS

www.twodaycoffee.co.uk

MAP.Nº 170
ROUND HILL ROASTERY
Unit 14, Midsomer Enterprise Park, Midsomer Norton, Somerset, BA3 2BB

www.roundhillroastery.com

MAP.Nº 171
SOUTH COAST ROAST
24 Richmond Hill, Bournemouth, Dorset, BH2 6EJ

www.thecaffienehustler.com

MAP.Nº 172
LITTLESTONE COFFEE
17 Norman Court, Budlake Road, Exeter, Devon, EX2 8PY

www.littlestonecoffee.co.uk

MAP.Nº 173
OLFACTORY COFFEE ROASTERS
The Old Brewery Yard, Lower Treluswell, Penryn, Cornwall, TR10 9AT

www.olfactorycoffee.co.uk

MAP.Nº 174
ORIGIN COFFEE ROASTERS
The Roastery, Wheal Vrose Business Park, Helston, Cornwall, TR13 0FG

www.origincoffee.co.uk

MANUMIT
COFFEE
ROASTERS
#17

MEET OUR COMMITTEE

Our *Independent Coffee Guide* committee is made up of a small band of leading coffee experts from across the region who have worked with Salt Media and the South West and South Wales' speciality community to oversee the creation of this book

TREVOR HYAM

Head barista, coffee trainer and front of house manager at The Plan Cafe in Cardiff, Trevor has been crafting coffee full time for over a decade. Coming fourth in the 2010 UK Barista Champs, he was one of the first baristas to serve speciality in the Welsh capital and has built a legion of caffeine converts at the city centre coffee shop. *'Coffee never ceases to excite and intrigue me; it's such a magical thing,'* says Trevor.

RICHARD BLAKE

Roasting with the original crew at Extract in the early days, Rich learnt most of what he knows about green coffee, trading, roasting and brewing at the Bristol roastery before leaving to launch his own business, Yallah Coffee, in 2014. As a keen surfer and outdoor adventurer, the Cornish countryside was a natural choice in which to house his lovingly-restored 1950s roaster. Sustainability, involvement in social enterprises and supporting communities reliant on the coffee chain are all high on the Yallah agenda.

CALLUM PARSONS

A relative newbie on the coffee block, Callum started his coffee career in 2014 at Extract Coffee Roasters. He's now its regional manager for the South West and Midlands, stocking coffee shops in his patch with lip-smackingly good beans. In 2017 he not only scooped the top spot in the South West heat of the UK Barista Championship, he also came fourth in the national competition. As fond of wine as coffee, Callum says: *'I often bring wine into a new conversation about speciality coffee as it's something many people can relate to in terms of how much it's affected by climate, origin and varietal.'*

DAVE STANTON

After catching the coffee bug Down Under, Dave returned to the UK eager to master the art of roasting. Fuelling his passion by professionally pouring brews by day, he spent his nights (for several years) experimenting on his home roaster. Dave finally took the leap into professional roasting in 2014, launching Crankhouse Coffee from his garage. Moving his operation to new premises in 2017 gave him more space in which to play. Crankhouse now stocks speciality coffee houses across the country with its collection of high quality blends and single origin beans.

COFFEE NOTES

Somewhere to save details of specific brews and
beans you've enjoyed

COFFEE NOTES

Somewhere to save details of specific brews and beans you've enjoyed

COFFEE NOTES

Somewhere to save details of specific brews and
beans you've enjoyed

INDEX